D0509700

SELF-IMPROVEMENT PUZZLES

TRAIN YOUR BRAIN

PRACTICAL PUZZLES TO IMPROVE BRAIN FUNCTION

Parragon

Bath · New York · Cologne · Melbourne · Delhi
Hong Kong · Shenzhen · Singapore

This edition published by Parragon Books Ltd in 2017

Parragon Books Ltd
Chartist House
15–17 Trim Street
Bath BA1 1HA, UK
www.parragon.com

Copyright © Parragon Books Ltd 2017
Written and designed by Any Puzzle Media Ltd

All rights reserved. No part of this publication may be reproduced, stored in a retrieval system or transmitted, in any form or by any means, electronic, mechanical, photocopying, recording or otherwise, without the prior permission of the copyright holder.

ISBN 978-1-4748-8137-1

Printed in China

CONTENTS

ABOUT THIS BOOK

We know how important it is to look after our bodies, as suggested by the enormous number of diet, exercise and general self-care books available. But it's equally as important to look after your brain. After all, without it you wouldn't be aware of anything at all, and it's important to keep challenging it so that it continues to learn.

This book provides a practical guide to looking after your brain. It isn't a reference book, designed to teach you interesting facts about what's going on upstairs. Instead, it focuses entirely on things that are directly *useful* to you in your everyday life. There are, for example, pages on the importance of sleep for learning, and on methods for solving difficult puzzles through what seems to be guesswork – all presented in a practical way, so you can apply them immediately to your day-to-day life.

The book also integrates a huge amount of fun brain-training material. The pages are packed with puzzles and exercises to try yourself, and most can be solved by writing directly in the book. Due to the wide range of material, there are sure to be many that you have never encountered before – but that's exactly the point. To train your brain you want to provide it with constant *new* challenges, so try everything out and do your best not to skip over anything that looks 'too difficult'. The chances are these are just the puzzles that will help you most of all!

The book is broken up into chapters, each consisting of a small number of separate sections. The sections can be read in any order, so there's no need to go by chapter, or by section within a chapter – everything is designed to be dipped into and dipped out of as you please, and as you have time. All the puzzles have solutions at the back, and you shouldn't be afraid to check them for 'inspiration' if you get stuck.

CAN YOU TRAIN YOUR BRAIN?

Your brain is constantly learning. Every new experience teaches your brain a little more about the world, and so over time you become smarter and smarter, and able to make faster, more sensible decisions. Many of these are not necessarily conscious decisions, but rather the natural result of your brain processing everything it's found out about the world to date. You train your brain every day, just by using your senses to experience the world around you.

So you can certainly train your brain in the general sense. But under the 'brain training' banner, it is often claimed that your brain can learn to make smarter, better decisions about things it hasn't directly experienced, and that this can be done simply by practising other, seemingly unrelated tasks. Some claim that playing the same simple games over and over will lead to a wide range of mental benefits, while others say that this is nonsense. The truth probably lies between the two extremes – exposing your brain to new and novel activities does, indeed, teach it general truths about the world and how to respond to new stimuli, and sometimes these can help your brain with completely unrelated activities. But it's also likely to be the case that once you have played the same, identical game a few dozen times that your iterative mental improvement from each successive play of the game will decrease just as your day-to-day improvement at the game itself also becomes steadily smaller and smaller.

Good brain training, therefore, involves challenging yourself with a constant diet of new and novel tasks. The more variety your brain encounters, the better. It's the new experiences that teach it the most, and so for the greatest mental improvement you should avoid repeating unchanging tasks. If you aren't consciously needing to stop and think, perhaps the subconscious parts of your brain also aren't being sufficiently challenged?

TRAIN YOUR BRAIN WITH THIS BOOK

This book is designed to provide just such a challenge – an incredibly varied range of puzzles, games and activities to help keep your grey matter in top condition. You could, of course, also find this challenge by traveling the world, learning foreign languages, or taking up a new musical instrument, but these aren't luxuries that all of us have the time – or money – for, and so, for the rest of us, that's where this book comes in.

Chapters two to four cover many of the general behaviours of your brain that you might not be aware of. Some of these can be critically important to know about, so you can make safer, faster choices in high-stress or other unusual situations. Chapter five then introduces you to the creative side of your brain, which is incredibly powerful – whether you consider yourself 'creative' or not. This is then followed by chapters on language skills, math, reasoning and spatial awareness.

Each chapter is broken down into sections, and each section of the book includes both an introduction as well as day-to-day practical tips to help build your brain skills in that area. Most sections also include some specific puzzles that are related to that area, which you can use to test out your new skills right away. Of course, the truth is that you will in reality be using a mixture of skills for every puzzle. For example, every decision you make uses 'reasoning', so these headings are there simply to help classify and break down the material – they shouldn't be taken as a literal description of the only activity that is going on when attempting a particular puzzle. This notwithstanding, each chapter contains puzzles where the primary focus is on the corresponding skills, so if you want to work on your map-reading skills then the spatial awareness chapter would be the one to turn to.

PUZZLES FOR FUN BRAIN TRAINING

Moments of high emotion can be very memorable, but your brain generally learns best when it is relaxed and not under stress. It stands to reason, therefore, that the best brain-training activities should also minimize stress. It's good to challenge yourself but, once it turns into frustration, your brain will start to learn that the activity you are engaged in should be avoided where possible. Positive reinforcement, through fun and entertaining brain training, is therefore beneficial.

All of the puzzles and challenges in this book have been designed to be fun. You won't find any long lists of sums to complete, or the same type of puzzle repeated over and over again, but rather a variety of tasks designed to make you think but without causing any deep frustration. If this ever ceases to be the case, you should put the puzzle aside and try another. Come back to it later and see if you can make progress, or turn to the solutions at the back and write in part of the solution to make it easier. In some cases, you could also think about *why* the solution at the back must be correct – although this isn't helpful for all puzzles. This same advice also works if you aren't sure about the rules – check the solved puzzle to see what the instructions mean, then pop back to the actual puzzle and give it a go yourself.

RELAXATION

It's important to try to relax while you work through the puzzles. Of course, simply *wishing* to be relaxed is unlikely to work and may even have the opposite effect, but there are various techniques you can try to help you get there. Any activity you enjoy in your free time is often a good start, whether that's sports, arts, games or even just reading. Laughter is a great relaxant too, so a favourite sitcom can even be a useful tool for helping you to prepare for better brain training.

Other methods of relaxation include trying to calm your breathing by taking longer, deeper breaths, although this should be done only in moderation and it should be stopped immediately if you start to feel light-headed or have any other side effects.

Light physical exercise, even as simple as just getting up and walking around a room while attempting to use as many muscles as possible, can also help you relax. A change of position can help you relax both physically *and* mentally.

Perhaps surprisingly, simply forcing yourself to smile can also help relax you – there is such a strong link between happiness and smiling, that just the act of smiling can help you to feel happy.

THE MOZART EFFECT

Good relaxation techniques for brain training can also help get your brain in a suitable state for learning. A particularly effective one for many people is simply to listen to music. Indeed, the effect of music on helping to put people into a state where they demonstrate better use of their mental faculties is known popularly as the 'Mozart Effect'.

Despite the name, music for priming your brain does not need to be by Mozart, but simply any kind of music that helps you to feel relaxed and yet doesn't send you to sleep. Just as many people find upbeat music helps them to work out physically, so positive and uplifting music helps your brain to work to the best of its ability too. It's important to note, however, that the 'Mozart Effect' does not mean that listening to music just by itself will make you any smarter.

FOCUS – AND DISTRACTIONS

A distracted brain does not learn as well as a brain that is concentrating on the task in hand. Although your brain carries on many different thought processes simultaneously, it is impossible to *consciously* think about multiple things – although we may think we do, in reality we are simply switching between different thoughts in quick succession. Studies have shown that even those people who think they are 'good multitaskers' do not work as well when they do multiple things at once as when they properly concentrate.

DISTRACTIONS

Distractions come in many different forms. There are audible distractions, such as chatter, noise, alarms or even just the click of a computer keyboard. There are physical distractions, such as an uncomfortable chair or desk, a breeze from an open window or even a room that is too hot or too cold. There can be distracting smells, for example from food or drinks, and there can even be distracting tastes that linger on from previous consumption. And then of course there are visual distractions, which run the gamut from email notifications through to people waving for your attention! Of course you cannot control all of these things, but even so when you are trying to 'get things done' you should do what you can reasonably and safely do to minimize them. Shut the door and turn off email or social media alerts, if you can, and find a comfortable position to work from.

FOCUS

Even if we eliminate most distractions, we still need to focus. It's very easy for our minds to drift, and indeed many of us find ourselves perfectly capable of spending a day doing 'work' without actually getting any real work done – if we have the opportunity. It's amazing how many distracting activities we can find to spend time on, whether it's reading news, chatting online with friends or simply doing easy, unimportant work while avoiding what really needs to get done.

Often the hardest part of a task seems to be the getting started, because, typically, once we have overcome the initial inertia against beginning something new, keeping going seems much easier. If this is a problem for you, there are various methods that can help avoid this problem, such as deliberately jumping right into the middle of a task. While it may make logical sense to begin at the start of a report, essay or other project, often the mental pressure of having the 'entire thing' to do feels too overwhelming, leading us to put off any attempts to actually get going. It's much better to do *something*, and then, having got past the 'getting started' hurdle, it's considerably easier to jump back and work on the beginning section of a task, if it's necessary to do so. From this point, maintaining focus often proves easier.

GETTING THINGS DONE
If you find it hard to avoid distractions and get focused, try these tips:

- Make a prioritized list of things you have to do, and put deadlines on it – then display the list somewhere where you can hold yourself, or have someone else hold you, to account for those deadlines.

- Break complex tasks down into a series of much smaller targets, the same way a company would distribute work among many employees. It's much easier to tackle a small, discrete problem than worry about the whole thing at once.

- Try to set aside enough time to complete each individual task you work on, rather than leaving them half-finished – sometimes it can be tricky to pick up exactly where you left off, leading to frustration.

- If you can, complete one project before starting the next.

FOCUS PUZZLES

These puzzles will require your full attention to solve.

1. Place digits from 1 to 9 into each white square so that no number
    repeats in any row, column or bold-lined 3×3 box. Shaded squares
    should remain empty, and can therefore represent different digits
    depending if they are considered as part of a row, column or box.

							6		2
		3	7					8	9
	4		9	6				7	
8			3		2	5			1
	3			7			9		
1		6	8		4	2			
	5				8		2		
3				7	4				
4		7							

2. Place an 'X' or an 'O' into each box so that no lines of four or more
    'X's or 'O's are formed – not even diagonally.

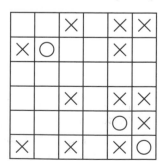

3. Draw solid lines to divide the grid to form a complete set of standard dominoes, with exactly one of each domino. A '0' represents a blank on a traditional domino. Use the check-off chart to keep track of the dominoes you have already placed.

1	4	4	1	1	3	0	5
1	3	6	3	3	2	2	6
6	5	0	3	2	3	1	5
6	6	4	1	4	6	0	2
0	2	1	2	2	5	5	0
2	4	3	3	6	4	4	0
1	5	5	4	5	0	6	0

0	1	2	3	4	5	6	
							0
							1
							2
							3
							4
							5
							6

4. Place a 0 or 1 in each empty square, so that there are an equal number of each digit in every row and column. Reading along a row or column, there may be no more than two of the same digit in succession. For example, 10011001 would be a valid row, but 10001101 would not be valid due to the three '0's in succession.

					0		0
		1		0	0	1	
			1				
0			0		0		
		1		0			1
				0			
	1	1	0		1		
1		0					

5. In the completed puzzle above, how many times does the sequence '010' appear, either horizontally or vertically?

SLEEP – AND CONSCIOUS THOUGHT

If we don't get enough sleep then of course we get tired, but the effects of this can be far more serious than just an urge to close our eyes. Studies have shown that sleep deprivation can have a similar effect to being drunk, and what's more, just as with inebriation, we might not even be aware of it at the time. Those with safety critical jobs usually have mandated rest periods for this very reason, since our bodies physically require sleep to maintain full mental competence.

At a lesser level, lack of sleep can have a range of lesser debilitating effects. It makes it harder to concentrate, and we are rarely at our sharpest. It also means we are less likely to spot mistakes we make, so often, if we slept for even a short while and then continued, we'd actually make faster progress than simply plodding on. And, of course, it is much less pleasant to be doing most things while tired.

MANAGING SLEEP

Maintaining a good sleep pattern is important, and even if it isn't always possible it should still be something you continually aspire to. Sleep also doesn't just need to be overnight – studies have shown that it is perfectly natural to have two separate sleeping periods during each 24-hour period, as for example some societies in hotter countries do with their afternoon siestas, although they have also shown that *more* than two periods of sleep won't work for most people.

Sleeping to a regular schedule also makes it easier to fall asleep quickly, since your body gets into a natural rhythm, and sometimes to wake feeling fresher too. Minimizing disturbances at sleep time is also wise, as is allowing yourself a brief period of time before closing your eyes when you are winding down a little. Otherwise, sometimes you'll find your mind full of thoughts about whatever you have just been dealing with, which can make it hard to get to sleep. Some people find that meditation, which can take the form of prayers if appropriate to your beliefs, also helps in this regard.

If you regularly have trouble sleeping you should consult an expert, since an accumulated lack of sleep can lead to significant mental health issues, quite apart from also being extremely frustrating!

YOUR UNCONSCIOUS MIND

Sleep also has some less obvious tricks up its cerebral sleeve. Firstly, it forms a key part of the process of storing memories. During sleep, your brain rehearses and re-examines the events of the day, learns from them and files away both the memories and the lessons it can take from the memories. If your sleep is impaired, you literally are less able to learn, and less able to remember what you have tried to learn.

Another amazing feature of sleep is that your brain will carry on processing the things you have thought about during the day – *without* your conscious knowledge of this. So if you are stuck on a particularly thorny problem, or have run short of ideas for how to make progress on a task, then try sleeping on it. It's genuinely good advice, because your unconscious mind is entirely capable of coming up with new solutions, which you will then find seemingly magically popping into your mind at hopefully opportune moments.

Indeed, much of our thought is inevitably completely unconscious – we can of course perform complex activities, such as driving, without consciously thinking about every manoeuvre, but our brains can do more than just apply learned procedures. Helping ensure that your brain gets enough sleep, has minimal distractions, and is in a relaxed state, all go a significant way to helping you think genuinely smarter thoughts.

SLEEP PUZZLES

If you get stuck on one of the following puzzles, try sleeping on it. They are all the type of puzzle where an insight might arrive when you least expect it to do so.

6. The day before yesterday I was 8 years old. Next year I'm going to be 11 years old. How can this be?

7. If Cowboy Bill rode into town on Friday, and rode out two days later on Friday, how can that possibly be true?

8. I have a bottle of lemonade that I have started drinking. There's more than half left but it isn't full. I've promised to leave exactly half a bottle for my friend. How can I be sure to do this, without making use of any other item to help measure it?

9. I'm holding a horse race but I want there to be a twist on the usual proceedings: the horse that comes in last will win. I don't want the race to last forever, so what can I do to persuade the jockeys to ride normally?

10. My pet hamster has got stuck in a hole in the ground, and I can't reach in to get it out. Can you think of a simple and safe way to get it out without hurting it?

11. It's pitch dark and you have a wooden splint, a candle and an oil lamp. There is only one match, so what do you light first?

12. If you pick up a scarf, how can you tie a knot in it without letting go of either end?

13. How do you put your left hand into the right pocket, and your right hand into the left pocket, of a pair of jeans without crossing your arms?

14. Between sunset and sunrise, I got out of bed 120 times, and yet I managed to sleep more than 8 hours between each and every one of the times that I got up. How can this be true?

15. If I tell you that I know someone who predicts the future, how can it possibly be the case that I am telling the truth?

16. A father gave his son a family heirloom, and a different father gave his son two family heirlooms. Yet there were only two heirlooms in total – how can this be true?

17. We can all agree that one comes before two, but how can two come after three and four before one?

18. How can you stand over a bare concrete floor and drop an uncooked egg for a metre without it breaking? You cannot modify the egg in any way.

19. When you add these to a box, the lighter it becomes – and yet the box stays empty. What are they?

20. If I go for a walk into a forest, what is the furthest distance I can get from the edge of the forest, expressed as a fraction of the entire width of the forest?

21. You are in a house with fantastic southern views from all four sides, and see a bear. What colour is the bear?

22. You have four identical coins on the table in front of you. How can you arrange them so that every coin is simultaneously touching all of the other coins?

DEALING WITH STRESS

We all experience stress in our lives from time to time, and it can be an important biological cue to help us focus on a pressing problem. However, in many cases it can also devolve into an ongoing source of anxiety which starts to corrode many aspects of our lives, making it hard to get anything done, and damaging important relationships.

If stress starts to take over your life then it is essential to do something about it. This can either take the form of tackling the source of the stress, if possible, or learning to manage the stress itself. The one thing you should never do is to ignore it – if you are continually under stress, your brain is less able to learn and you are far more susceptible to both physical and mental illness.

SIMPLE METHODS TO LESSEN STRESS

Laughter really is a great medicine, at least in terms of making you feel better. It has been proven to alleviate stress, and so if you are feeling stressed then you could do worse than watch something that will make you laugh.

Another great way of relieving stress is physical exercise. Just going for a walk can help, as can more strenuous physical exercise such as working out in a gym, or going swimming. Even just the change of scene can help, since it forces you to refocus, at least briefly, on the physical world around you.

Social contact is also an amazingly powerful tonic. Humans are social animals, and the vast majority of us are much happier in the company of others than on our own. Social media can provide some of this feeling of connectedness, but nothing beats physical contact with other humans.

Ironically, stress, particularly the work-based type, often leads to us working longer hours and having less social time, which in turn increases our stress and makes us less effective at our job. Just as with sleep, taking a break can often lead to faster, better work than simply trying to always power through.

Perversely, deliberately slowing down can sometimes also help with certain sources of stress. Feelings of constant pressure can sometimes be reduced by the act of simply managing your time. Avoid doing everything at breakneck speed, or packing too much into each day. This creates a feeling of control which can help you feel more empowered and less stressed. Just gently slowing your breathing for a minute can be enough, even, to reduce stress – giving your addled brain a moment to escape from the stressful thoughts circulating inside it.

Some people fall back on drugs such as alcohol to help them relax, but while these chemical 'solutions' can in some cases provide short-term escape from stress they are certainly not long-term solutions, and those who come to rely on them will typically end up with significant health problems – both mentally and physically.

CREATING AN ANTI-STRESS STRATEGY

For longer-term methods of avoiding stress, try to restructure your time, if you can, to minimize the stressful periods:

- Set aside 'relaxation' time, or decide that when you are relaxing you will definitely *not* think about your sources of stress, whether they be work deadlines or family-related issues. No matter your responsibilities to others, if you don't look after yourself then you won't be able to help them. You can't be on 24-hour call every day.

- Set a schedule so you know when you will be dealing with the stress-related issues, and try to avoid thinking about them at any other time.

- If you're worrying you might forget to do things, unload them from your brain and make a written list – this simple act can really help.

THE SCIENCE OF GUESSING

Young children have little or no fear of failure, which is an important tool for learning to handle the world. They'd never learn to walk if they were afraid of falling. This childhood fearlessness extends far beyond the toddler years – for example, learning to ride a bicycle as a child is much less nerve-racking than as an adult, where the fear of falling typically becomes much more dominant.

In life in general, fear of failure often holds people back from trying new things. This doesn't just apply to physical fear, but to conscious thought too, limiting what we feel we can do. We *think* we can't do things, and so we don't try. How many times have you heard someone say, 'I can't do that', when perhaps they actually could if they really tried?

As many people age they start to develop a learned helplessness in the face of unfamiliar tasks. This instinctive avoidance of the new shows up in the logical inconsistency of someone who claims they 'can't do maths' while knowing exactly how much they have in the bank, or the pensioner who avoids learning how to send email while continuing to solve complex daily crosswords.

Children learn through experimentation and guesswork, and a limited fear of failure. Children don't yet know what they can and can't do, so give a child a puzzle book and he or she will happily try any puzzle they turn to, whereas an adult will look for the puzzles they already know how to do and will often skip those that are less familiar.

MAKING PROGRESS BY GUESSING

Next time you're stuck on a puzzle, or aren't sure how to handle a situation, try just guessing. When you guess on a puzzle you are usually making a choice without any good reason, and in life in general you may have no idea if something is a sensible choice or not. But, simply by trying out the guess, you are likely to learn more than you knew before. Even if the guess proves itself wrong, or not good in some way, you gain knowledge that will often help make your *next* guess a better one. And in some cases, such as with puzzles, finding out what definitely is *not* correct also moves you a step to the actual solution, plus it can help you to spot patterns that you hadn't previously seen.

An experimental approach works for many aspects of life. If you're a writer unable to put down the first paragraph, or come up with a plot, then make a guess at what will work, even if you feel sure you won't stick with it, and get going. It's a better option than never writing anything. Or if you're looking to move to a new place, or change jobs, but have no idea where to begin, try exploring new options by looking at random places on a map, or arbitrary job listings. When you overthink big decisions, they can feel overwhelming. Making a small start at them, no matter how insignificant or pointless it may seem, will help you begin to narrow down your options – and will get your brain ticking over too. You might find that your brain comes up with new ideas without any extra help, once you get it thinking more positively about a subject.

LEARNING THROUGH GUESSING

The secret to guessing is not to worry about whether your guess will prove to be 'right' or not, or otherwise you will be back at the same problem you had before. The key thing is to just do it – it's only through trying a guess, and possibly 'failing', that you will make progress. But that word, 'failing', is a negative word from a previous mindset – when you guess deliberately then any guess that proves ultimately not to be the way forward is in fact simply a new way of learning. Or, rather, the old way of learning that you once used as a small child.

PUZZLES – TAKE A GUESS!

All of these puzzles can be solved by making guesses and experimenting.

23. The classic guessing puzzle. Solve this maze by finding a route from the entrance at the top to the exit at the bottom.

24. Join *all* of the dots using horizontal and vertical lines to form a single loop. The loop must not cross over or touch itself in any way.

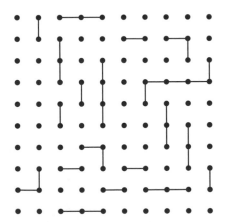

25. Draw a series of separate paths, each connecting a pair of identical numbers. No more than one path can enter any grid square, and a path cannot re-enter a square. Paths can travel horizontally and vertically, but never diagonally.

1	2										
3	4										4
		2									
	5		6	7							6
									7	8	
	5		1	9				9		10	
11		10									
	12		13							12	
			3	14		14	13				
	15							8	15		
			16						16		
		11									

26. Draw borders along some grid lines to divide the grid into a set of rectangles, so that each rectangle contains exactly one number. The number inside each rectangle must be precisely equal to the number of grid squares that the rectangle contains. Note that the term 'rectangle' also includes squares.

			4			2			
								4	2
			3						
					8			8	
		12	2						
	4		16					12	
							15		
	3			2			3		

FRESH THINKING

From time to time, most of us get stuck in a rut in our thinking. Usually this results in assumptions we aren't aware we're making, which end up limiting the scope of the solutions we are able to come up with.

An outside perspective is often useful in challenging assumptions, although there is an associated challenge in *accepting* that outside view when it contradicts our own. Many people will instinctively cling to what they already believe, even if another person's point is entirely valid. It's good advice to avoid jumping to conclusions, and take time to let your brain digest any points before dismissing them.

Ideas that seem ridiculous or useless do themselves sometimes lead to fresh perspectives on existing problems. Even if you don't bring in an external view, it's useful to come up with solutions that you *don't* think will work – even just explaining to yourself out loud why you 'know' they won't work can help you make breakthroughs in your thinking.

Indeed, talking out loud is a great way of moving on your thought process. When you vocalize thoughts you make your brain think in a different way, and it's amazing how often the very act of explaining something – even to yourself – can lead to moments of revelation. In fact, if you can't explain something clearly then you perhaps don't understand it clearly either, so testing yourself in this way is a good method for discovering weaknesses in your thinking.

THE WISDOM OF CROWDS

Aristotle wrote about the wisdom of crowds in *Politics*, around 2,500 years ago. So it's not a new notion that two heads are better than one, and certainly it's the case that groups can be more creative and bring far more experience to a situation than any one individual can hope to do. In the best situations, individuals can bounce ideas off each other, iteratively improving them. So it's always good to seek a second opinion, so long as you don't let these opinions unduly sway you, unless of course you know they are backed up by far more expertize than you have.

There's a danger with groups, however, that people will be afraid to speak up in front of certain others, or that those who are most ignorant may not realize their ignorance and come to dominate the discussion – or even may do so deliberately. So group discussions need to be carefully managed.

THE WISDOM OF YOU

If you are knowledgeable about a subject area, try not to doubt yourself too much. It's fine to challenge your own assumptions, but when presenting your thoughts or conclusions to others then it is best to appear as confident as possible. You might feel that you need to explain all of the pros and cons of a proposal, and perhaps in some contexts you truly might need to, but in very many cases you will sadly do yourself a disservice by being too intellectually rigorous in a presentation.

As social creatures, we instinctively trust other people who *seem* trustworthy, and who appear to know what they are doing. Ironically, if you explain potential pitfalls you will be less convincing to non-experts than a person who does not. The confident, ignorant person appears more capable – look, their idea has *no* potential pitfalls, says the instinctive part of our brain. Don't give a detailed explanation to people who will be perfectly happy with a simplified version – if they don't follow they will judge you as less competent, and adding unnecessary details only invites potential objections that could otherwise have been avoided.

It's also important to note that usually we don't need a *perfect* solution, but simply a *good enough* solution. This is not to say that aiming for excellence is a bad idea, but that overcomplicating things rarely helps in the long run. Often you will convince someone more with a simple, slightly flawed argument than a complex, flawless one.

NEW EXPERIENCES

The more we challenge our brains, the wiser we get. It's easy to get into a routine where one day is very similar to another, but the more we can mix in variety then the better we will feel and the happier our brains will be.

Introducing variety can be as simple as taking a different route on a regular journey. Leave a few minutes earlier and go a slightly different way, or if you like to walk then even just try walking in the opposite direction to normal on a familiar route.

When you are out and about, try to look around you and take in the sights – don't let familiarity with an area blind you to what's right in front of you. It might be surprising what you see that you've never noticed before. And even if you're a particularly observant person, you probably don't look up very much. In older towns and cities there can often be interesting features higher up on buildings which are well worth discovering.

Of course, the more you can mix up your routine the better. Even if you work during the day, perhaps there are things you can change, whether it's going somewhere else for lunch, reading a different newspaper or website, or listening to a different radio station or music as you travel.

FOREIGN LANGUAGES

Many languages have been developed by communities in sometimes very different parts of the world to our own, and so those languages often include concepts and thoughts that can be quite alien to someone who has had no exposure to those peoples. Just by learning another language, ideally one not very closely related to our own, we are exposed to these other concepts. As we become more fluent, we can then discover new ways of thinking that are facilitated by those other languages. Even if you only learn the basics of a foreign language, it can still act as a gateway to becoming familiar with a range of ideas that help open you up to a raft of new experiences. And it's also a great new challenge for your brain.

TRAVEL TO UNFAMILIAR PLACES

You don't necessarily need to travel far to visit somewhere that can seem very different, but if you have the time and money to visit somewhere distant and exotic then your brain will certainly enjoy the trip. Taking in entirely new sights, sounds and situations will provide a significant mental stimulus – not to mention challenge – that can benefit you for the rest of your life. The more you experience the world around you, whether that's on a local or more distant level, the better you will be able to cope with new experiences when they come at you unexpectedly.

LEARN TO PLAY A MUSICAL INSTRUMENT

Learning to play a musical instrument can be one of the greatest pleasures in life. Perhaps not everyone who listens to you in the early stages may agree with this, but the mental benefit to you can be profound, both in terms of the learning you will engage in and also the relaxation it can bring. Even if you already play an instrument, you could learn one that's very different – for example, if you play the guitar then try the piano, and vice versa. Or even just challenge yourself to play in new ways on an instrument you already play, such as trying to 'play by ear' if you normally read music, or try improvising if you have never done so.

TAKE UP A NEW HOBBY

There are so many activities in the world to choose from that it can be overwhelming to choose one, but if you feel you could benefit from more social contact then why not look locally to see what nearby groups offer, and get involved? Even if you aren't sure you'll enjoy something, there's usually little harm in giving it a go, especially if the costs are minimal.

Whatever it is you decide to do, the important thing is that if you are not enjoying it then you should move on to something else. Remember that a stressed or unhappy brain does not learn well, so if you aren't sufficiently motivated then there is likely to be minimal benefit from the activity.

NEW CHALLENGES

Try these new types of puzzle, and see how you get on with something that you aren't already familiar with.

27. Draw 1x2 and 1x3 rectangular blocks along the grid lines such that each number is contained in exactly one block. The number in each block reveals the total count of white spaces the block can slide into. Shapes that are wider than they are tall slide horizontally left and right, and shapes that are taller than they are wide slide vertically up and down.

See the example solution to the right to understand how this works. For example consider the 2 in the top row – it can move into 2 spaces. Meanwhile, the 0 at the bottom-right cannot move into any spaces; the spaces above it do not count because it does not slide this way.

28. What is the simplest change you can make to this equation in order to make it correct?

29. Draw a fence to protect the sheep ('S') from the wolves ('W') by joining dots with a single continuous line so that all sheep are inside the area and all wolves outside it. Use only horizontal or vertical lines, and the fence cannot touch, cross or overlap itself in any way. The numbers 1, 2 and 3 indicate that the fence must run along 1, 2 or 3 sides of the square formed by the 4 dots around the number.

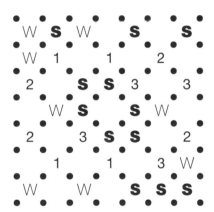

30. Place 1 to 9 once each into this grid. Black dots indicate pairs of squares where one digit is exactly twice the value of the other, such as 3 and 6. White dots indicate consecutive digits, such as 3 and 4. No dot means neither applies. If both a black *and* white dot could be used, only one is given.

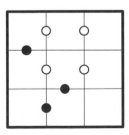

31. Complete this spiral crossword, where the clues read both inwards *and* outwards simultaneously.

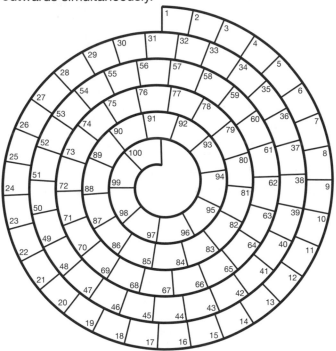

Inward

1-6	Gilded
7-9	Pump an accelerator
10-14	Gawks at
15-18	Possible hair infection
19-22	Dispatched
23-27	Chat-show group
28-30	Prune
31-37	Sweet course
38-42	Allied
43-46	Devotional painting
47-51	Type of heron
52-57	Claim
58-60	Cattle chew this
61-65	Wear down
66-73	Accepted etiquette
74-78	Raw vegetable dish
79-81	Tennis-court divider
82-86	Jobs
87-91	Angry
92-96	Old photo colour
97-100	Elitist

Outward

100-95	Dwarf tree
94-89	Former Spanish currency
88-84	Dangers
83-78	Be present at
77-74	Sadly
73-70	Railway train
69-63	Underwater missile
62-57	Lessen
56-54	Hairstyling substance
53-49	Afterwards
48-41	Racial extermination
40-31	Suffering from great anxiety
30-25	Powder from flowers
24-18	Relevance
17-12	Glittery Christmas material
11-4	Ruled
3-1	Captain's journal

32. Find a route from the lowest to the highest number, visiting all numbers in increasing numerical order. The route can only travel horizontally and vertically between squares, and it can't revisit any square. It can only cross itself on the marked bridges. All squares must be visited, and all bridges must be used in both directions. A small example is given.

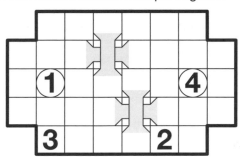

33. Shade some squares, so that no two shaded squares are adjacent, except diagonally, and all unshaded squares form a single continuous area. Any single horizontal or vertical row of unshaded cells cannot cross more than one bold line. Numbered squares may or may not be shaded, but always give the precise amount of shaded squares in a bold-lined region.

A VERY SOCIAL BRAIN

One of the most fundamental desires of most of us is to fit in with the people around us. We worry about embarrassing ourselves in front of others, we worry about appearing strange, and we worry that we are not as good as other people in a whole myriad of ways.

Social media, while allowing some people to feel more connected with others than they might previously have done, also brings with it a whole host of new pressures. The vast majority of people will create a sanitized, polished version of themselves online, whether they do this consciously or not. They will appear to be happier, prettier, richer, more organized, better travelled, more educated and generally wiser than they probably are in reality – and that's just the honest ones! Some people go further and invent a fantasy version of themselves, whether it's through editing photos to remove wrinkles, claiming to be places they aren't, or making claims of happiness they don't truly feel. This doesn't make these people terrible human beings, but what it *does* mean is that when we compare *ourselves* it can lead us to feel inferior or inadequate – even though we are not.

When reviewing stories about others online, whether of celebrities in the press or of friends on social media, we need to remind ourselves that these are sanitized, selected snippets from their lives, and we should never judge ourselves by comparison with these misleading excerpts.

THE JUDGEMENT OF OTHERS

We spend our lives worrying about what others think of us, when in reality the honest truth is that most people – even those reasonably close to us – notice a lot less about us than we might think, or even hope. Most people are so wrapped up in their own thoughts, worries and preoccupations that they devote little time to thinking about those of others. When you consider that this applies to those we know well, just consider how little those who don't know us at all will typically notice about us.

When out in public it is possible to be self-conscious about a whole host of body and other issues, when in reality most people will be paying you very little direct attention. They are probably wrapped up in their own thoughts, and more concerned about themselves. Of course there are occasional exceptions to this rule but, more often than not, from the point of view of strangers you are neither as interesting or as remarkable as you think – even though in reality we are *all* interesting and remarkable.

Studies have shown that people can do all manner of strange things while standing in view of sitting strangers, who then mostly remain entirely oblivious. So next time you think you have embarrassed yourself, try not to worry about it too much – the chances are that most people haven't even noticed. The *worst* thing you can do is draw attention to it – so *don't* apologize, unless you are absolutely certain it is necessary, and be sure not to apologize more than is needed.

BE POSITIVE

Apologizing in general is something many of us get wrong. If you think you have made a mistake, own up to it quickly and say so only briefly. Then move on, *and never mention it again*. If you keep apologizing you will simply make your action memorable, whereas if you handle it and then immediately carry on as if nothing had happened it will almost certainly be forgotten before long.

Be positive whenever you can. *Don't* talk yourself down – in most cases if you are able to self-criticize then you have already considered the pros and cons of an argument; there's no need to weaken your position in front of anyone else. They can think about it themselves if they wish, and people have an inherent tendency to trust those who appear most self-confident – even if they are entirely ignorant. Don't let too much knowledge about a subject make you appear less confident, through your knowledge of the risks, than someone who is broadly ignorant and just ploughs on blindly.

HIDDEN IN PLAIN SIGHT

These puzzles are all based on the concept of things being less obvious than you'd expect.

34. Can you find this plus shape hidden inside this network of lines? It can be rotated or at a different size, but in every other way its shape will be identical.

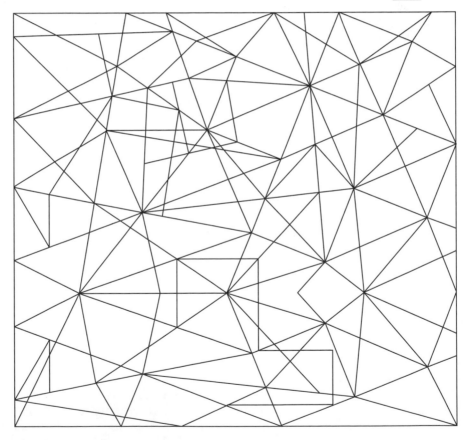

35. Each of the following sentences contains a hidden flower. Can you find them all?

- Never a big fan of synth-pop, Pythagoras preferred to theorize
- After paying in his gyros, Euclid came up with some maths stuff
- The ballerina wore a tutu, lipstick and not much else
- Bengali lychees taste better than average, or so they claim
- The Yugoslav end erased much Eastern European progress
- Scrape onyx from a mine seam and you might get rich

36. How many times does the sequence 121 appear in this string of numbers?

121212221212212122121221121212212112121212111221

37. How quickly can you find each of the two patterns in the overall grid?

THE CERTAINTY OF BEING WRONG

We all jump to conclusions from time to time, but it isn't always our fault. Our brains are wired to make certain decisions as fast as possible, since they could be critical to our survival. But there's just one problem – in our modern lives, usually we aren't in any immediate danger, and these snap decisions can actually lead to problems.

FALSE LEARNING

We learn by spotting patterns, associating certain events with certain outcomes. This is true all life long. As children we learn to walk by experimenting and sometimes falling – but along the way, our brains connect the dots between action and outcome, until it becomes entirely effortless. Unfortunately, this ability for our brains to spot patterns is so powerful that it can lead to us being 'sure' of things that are entirely false.

One example of false learning is casinos. Many people convince themselves they have spotted patterns in game outcomes and bet accordingly, even when those outcomes are in truth essentially random and therefore are unpredictable.

Historically, people would look for – and think they had found – patterns and secret codes in all kinds of places. Isaac Newton devoted much of his life not to his lasting achievements in maths and physics but rather to searching for the hidden code that he was sure ran throughout the Bible. The fact is that the brain will tend to spot patterns if you look for them, even if those patterns are nothing more than random chance. Out of the infinite number of *possible* patterns, one or more of them are likely to be present in almost any material. Finding those patterns, therefore, is entirely a matter of searching long enough – their presence is not in any way meaningful.

EXPECTATION BIAS

Just as with patterns, we often see the things we expect to see. If you believe in ghosts and the wind blows a curtain, you may take it as evidence of a spiritual presence. Inaudible deep bass sounds can make candles flicker even in the absence of air currents, but this is just a physical phenomenon. It is very easy to work from a conclusion back to a start point, when in fact it would only be meaningful to work the other way. Although lemons are yellow, not everything that is yellow is a lemon.

One particularly problematic area for expectation bias is medical procedures. For many more minor ailments we will usually get better by ourselves, especially if we think positively about them. This means that people unknowingly given placebo drugs, such as sugar pills, are often absolutely certain they have got better due to the pill, when in fact it had no effect.

This unwitting bias forms the basis of most alternative medicine practices, and while these can sometimes be mentally beneficial, due to the belief that we will get better, they sadly cannot help in more complex situations. People who undergo medical treatment, but stop to try alternative medicines, might associate any belated benefits from the medical treatment with the alternative techniques instead. This 'false learning' is just part of your brain's natural learning abilities – but it's important to remember that correlation is not causation. Just because one thing follows another, it doesn't mean it caused it.

SELECTION BIAS

Similarly, our brains love to cherry-pick results from the past. We remember when things turned out the way we expected, and forget about the times when we were wrong. It's important to be aware of this effect, so we know to challenge our own assumptions.

CHALLENGING EXPECTATIONS

Each of these puzzles will require you to challenge your assumptions.

38. One hundred prisoners are lined up all in a row, facing the same direction. Each prisoner is wearing a hat, which is either red or blue. Each prisoner can only see the people in front of them, and which colour hat each of them is wearing. They cannot see their own hat, or anyone behind them.

A prison officer enters the room, goes up to the prisoner at the back of the line, and asks them to say out loud either 'red' or 'blue', to predict whether they are wearing a red or blue hat. If they answer correctly, they will be released from prison. If they answer incorrectly, they will be confined for life. In either case, they must stay in line and the officer will not confirm whether they are correct or incorrect but will simply move onto the next person in line, carrying on down the line until they reach the front of the line.

The prisoners are told in advance what will happen, and have time to discuss and agree a strategy. By using an optimal strategy, what is the maximum number of prisoners that can be *guaranteed* to be released?

39. A waiter gives out 100 glasses of water, but when he collects them back in he is able to combine the remains of the water in 10 glasses to make 1 full glass. How many glasses of water can he make from the 100 glasses he has collected back in?

40. A blind man is marooned on a desert island without any outside contact. He has two green pills and two yellow pills, and needs to take exactly one of each pill. How can he do this, even though he can't see the pills? The pills have no other perceptible differences.

41. Three friends are in a room, and each makes a contradictory statement:

- **Dave**: Exactly one of us is lying

- **Samuel:** Exactly two of us are lying
- **Diana**: Exactly three of us are lying

Which of the three friends is actually telling the truth?

42. A dog fastened via a long leash to a tree is preventing me returning to my car. The dog blocks my every move when I try to step within the radius of the leash. What can I do, without hurting the dog, to reach my car?

43. It looks like you could create a circle by drawing a continuous line through the centres of these eight dots, but is it possible to join them all while making a square?

UNHELPFUL BRAIN RESPONSES

Due to our evolutionary history as prey for larger animals, we have some unhelpful primitive responses. From time to time we need to consciously override these using the more modern parts of our brain.

EXPECT THE UNEXPECTED

One primitive behaviour is the tendency to freeze, both physically and mentally, in moments of extreme pressure. This might be panic in the face of an imminent collision, a sudden painful realization, or extreme challenge in other ways. This behaviour made sense when we were trying to avoid detection, but it is almost entirely useless in a modern context – and indeed can be extremely dangerous when physical peril is the trigger.

It may seem a very pessimistic thing to do, but it is actually a very good idea to consciously think through what you would do in various stressful situations – from threats of physical harm, such as a nearby fire or a rapidly approaching vehicle, through to sudden accusations against us made by others that may not have our best interests at heart. Our immediate instinctive responses are usually unhelpful, but rehearsing in advance what we might do helps us avoid and override the instinctive, primitive response, and better handle these critical situations – should they ever occur, of course, which hopefully they will not.

THINK FOR YOURSELF

Countless evidence exists to show that people will do very surprising things so as not to stand out from the crowd. When asked everyday trivia questions, such as for example whether London is the capital of England, most people would answer correctly in the positive. But put them in a group of actors where the ten people before them all answer 'no', and amazingly the majority of people will then *also* answer 'no'. So strong is the desire to conform, and act as the majority does, that we will start to question our own fundamental beliefs and knowledge.

It's especially important to be aware of this effect in potentially hazardous situations. For example, even if other people stay put when a fire alarm sounds, that doesn't mean you should too. If you think there's a chance it might be a real alarm, then you should act on it – what does it really matter that no one else does? You may be afraid of feeling 'stupid' if you act differently to others, but in a life-and-death situation you owe it to yourself to act as *you* think best, not as others think best. This doesn't mean you shouldn't try to help other people, if appropriate, but simply that it isn't safe to *assume* that others know any better – they don't, unless you have good reason to believe otherwise.

The opposite situation can also arise, where a mass outbreak of panic is caused by something trivial. We instinctively assume that 'the crowd' must be correct, when in reality this is not necessarily the case. This instinct derives from primitive behaviour that benefits a herd animal with less capable mental abilities than we possess. Once you know that in any stressful or hazardous situation your instinct will always be to copy others, you can learn to take a moment to override it – and think for yourself.

FALSE SENSE OF URGENCY

Many times in life we are presented with a false sense of urgency. Whether it's our brain falsely telling us we'd better eat that cake while we still have access to that wonderfully fatty food supply, or a sales person pretending that the apparent bargain in front of us won't still be there if we come back later, our brains are easily rushed into making decisions that they don't have to make. Our primitive fear of losing out on some vital resource outweighs the more considered approach that we should probably take instead. Even if we do occasionally lose out on something, it will probably be more than balanced for by the many times we avoid making a decision we later regret.

UNLEASH YOUR CREATIVITY

Maybe you are an accomplished artist, but there are many people who think that they 'aren't creative'. While it is true that not everyone can paint like Monet, or sculpt like Michelangelo, we are still all capable of being creative. Every time we work out a route from A to B, or indeed think of a solution to any problem, we are being creative. So there is no reason at all why we can't also channel this creativity into more artistic areas – in fact, the Oxford Dictionary of English defines 'artistic' as 'having natural creative skill', which in this sense covers everyone!

A significant problem many of us face in our attempts to be creative is overcoming the initial inertia of the blank page. Faced with the infinite scope of all that is possible, it's no surprise that we can find it hard to write the initial words, or draw the first lines. Luckily, there are a wide range of techniques that can be used to help, all of which are based on the idea of 'just getting going'. Once we have *something* on the page it can help trigger related ideas, or suggest the basis of a framework on which to build the rest. The reason we find these first steps so painful is that we often expect ourselves to decide what we are going to create in advance, but the truth in most creative situations is that the work will develop and evolve as it progresses – and even head off in completely unexpected directions. Trying to have a complete vision before you even begin is putting an unnecessary pressure on yourself.

ART

Art is anything you say it is, so the great thing about creative activities is that it's impossible to 'go wrong'. Many of us are our own harshest critics, but if we can learn to relax and not worry too much about the end result then even if we don't like where we end up, we can still enjoy the journey to get there. Giving your brain a chance to metaphorically breathe can help you relax, can lessen stress and can also make you feel good about yourself – especially if you discover a skill that you thought you didn't have.

Almost any activity could be classed as art, but the easiest way to get going is just to grab a pencil, scribble a few random lines on a page and then step back to see what it looks like. Our brains are so accomplished at spotting patterns that there's a good chance you'll think it looks a bit like *something* – and then you can either carry on building from that new idea, or draw a few more random lines and take a fresh look. Or of course you could deliberately create a patterned drawing, by repeating the same design continually across a page. If you do this then it doesn't really matter what the repeated pattern is, because the very act of repetition tends to lend an image a visually pleasing quality.

Other types of art to consider include:

- Origami – paper folding can be very therapeutic, and it's an easy way to end up with a rewarding 3D model that feels pretty substantial.

- Sculpting – not with stone, but with modelling clay or plasticine. Start by making abstract structures, or create a range of cartoon figures.

- Paper cutting – taking a sheet of paper, folding it up and then cutting sections out can result in various patterned pieces of paper. It's easy to do and the results can be surprisingly beautiful.

- Guided arts, such as colouring books or dot-to-dots. Even if the outlines are provided for you, there's still a lot of creative freedom to colour as you please. Or if even that feels a bit too much like hard work, you could try a colour-by-number book – the satisfaction from creating your own picture can be remarkable, especially if you haven't felt it since you were a child!

IT'S ALL IN THE DOTS

44. Start by joining the dots in increasing numerical order in this classic puzzle. An image will slowly emerge as you do so. You can then colour it in with your choice of colours if you so wish.

45. What if there are no numbers next to the dots? Give this puzzle a go even if you don't think it seems worth it – you might be surprised at what comes out of it. All you have to do is join the dots – but however you like, and not necessarily all together. Take a moment after you've drawn a few lines to see what the image is starting to look like – a face, or a monster, or a leaf, perhaps, and then if you wish you can start adding lines that build on that existing image. Or you could just join lines randomly, and colour the resulting areas.

CREATIVE WRITING

Many people feel that they 'have a novel inside them', but how many actually put pen to paper, or finger to keyboard, and get writing? Like most creative endeavours, it's typically the getting going that causes the greatest problems. This can either result in not getting started on a piece of writing at all, or it can mean that once you take a break you find it very hard to continue.

Writing is inherently a creative process, even if you are writing fact rather than fiction. The way that you choose to express ideas, and the words you use for that expression, are critical parts of how a reader will experience your message – and understand it, remember it and perhaps also be swayed by it, if you are aiming to convince a reader of a particular point.

GETTING GOING

In many forms of creative endeavour, one method of breaking a creative block is simply to do literally anything, and see if you are inspired. For factual writing this can work particularly well, because you usually know at least the general area that you want to write about. This means that even if you jump into the middle at a bit that's particularly easy to write, that's okay because at least you are working towards your end goal. You don't necessarily need to keep the text you write first, but it will help you decide how to structure and present your ideas.

For long-form creative writing, you will probably need to start at a higher level by deciding on the basics of a plot. But even when you do this, all the same principles apply. Rather than writing finished pieces of prose, you will be noting down characters or events, but the same tactic of starting at an arbitrary point and then fleshing it out as inspiration hits will still work. You should also not be afraid to be inspired by other creative works. After all, there are very few truly fresh novels, and there's no point in setting a goal so lofty that it becomes almost unattainable. Indeed, you could even start by using existing characters, settings or even basic plots and then write your own version of them – the novel *Fifty Shades of Grey* was first written as *Twilight* fan fiction, then modified for publication to remove any direct references. Whatever it takes to get you going is fair game – it is much easier to amend something you have already written than it is to fill in a completely blank page.

DON'T EXPECT PERFECTION

It's unreasonable to expect your early written works to be masterpieces. Maybe they will be, but most people improve with practice, just as we all do with respect to any other skill. Certainly, if you reread text you wrote some time ago you may well be surprised at the difference between your earlier work and your current level of writing.

So another key part of creative writing is simply to just keep trying. Each time you do you'll get better and better, and you'll learn from previous mistakes – such as a plot that was too restrictive, or a piece of factual text that was too broad in its ambition.

WRITE FOR YOURSELF

Creative activities, or at least those performed principally for the purpose of relaxation and fun, are most enjoyable when not taken too seriously. Try not to worry too much about what other people will think, so you can relax and let your brain be truly creative. If you write for yourself, you needn't care about anyone else's opinion – when it's your own creation, no one else can tell you you're wrong. Art is in any case purely in the eye of the beholder.

There are some simple creative writing activities on the following two pages, which should help ease you into the process. If you can handle these, you'll be ready to get started on the real thing!

CREATIVE WRITING ACTIVITIES

Write a second, rhyming line for each of these given lines. For example, you could rhyme 'The light of day awakes in me' with 'A craving for a cup of tea'.

46. From dawn to dusk on every day,

_____

47. The fallen leaves float gently down,

_____

48. The scent of summer wafting wide,

_____

49. The twin-hulled ship of fate was holed,

_____

Now try coming up with some punchlines for these jokes.

50. Why did the aardvark cross the road?

_____

51. What's the difference between a paper fastener and a horse stall?

_____

52. What do you call a one-eyed giant?

_____

53. Write a very short story that uses each of the following items:

Location: The south of France

Person: The king of Spain

Item: A diamond necklace

_____

_____

_____

_____

_____

_____

54. Invent your own place name for an imaginary island, located just off the coast of the equally imaginary continent of Austraferica:

_____

55. Create an imaginary monster. Give it a really evocative name, then go on to describe its features. What does it look like? Is it fearsome or friendly? Does it have any supernatural abilities, such as fire-breathing?

_____

_____

_____

_____

BUILDING CREATIVITY

Blank pages and canvases can present a challenge with getting started, so an alternative option is to pick a creative activity where you start with a set of pieces and then rearrange them. Even a small box of building bricks, for example, can be assembled into an incredibly large number of different structures, so this is nowhere near as restrictive as it may sound. This can also make it easier to experiment, and help avoid the creative block which can stem from an empty page.

One of the simplest of creative activities is to take a small number of flat pieces and arrange them into shapes, such as with tangram pieces. You can easily create your own set of tangrams by simply cutting up a square of paper as shown here. You can also trace the diagram if you prefer, and colour in each piece. Just colour the top side, and avoid flipping them over.

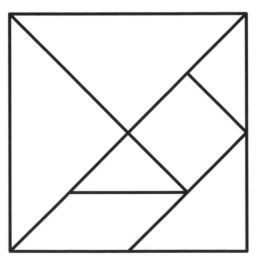

Once you've made your tangrams, try arranging them on a table or other surface to make various silhouettes. Can you make a house, or a goose, or a silhouette of a person?

BUILDING BLOCKS

With even more pieces you can make even more things, and if you step up from two dimensions to three dimensions then the possibilities literally expand in all directions. Manufacturers of interlocking toy blocks, such as LEGO®, provide sets of basic bricks that can be bought for free-form construction, and these provide both a fun and easy method of simply and quickly 'being creative'. And if you think you might be 'too old' for things such as this, it's worth noting that sales of LEGO® to adults account for a significant proportion of their revenue.

Adult versions of activities previously engaged in primarily by children have expanded enormously in recent years, with large numbers of colouring-in, dot-to-dot and other books of this type aimed specifically at adults now widely available. What these trends reveal is that it's simply societal conventions that have previously held back many adults from engaging in the things they enjoyed while growing up – which is a shame, because relaxing in these relatively simple ways is good for your brain.

CREATIVE PUZZLE-SOLVING

All around the world, 'escape rooms' have opened where adults can go and rush about for an hour trying to solve as many puzzles as they can, and in most cases 'escape' from the room before time is up. These are brilliant for your brain, combining creative thinking, physical exercise, social contact and novel exploration into a single activity. The possible downside is that they do tend to be quite expensive.

You don't have to head out to play challenging, sociable, thought-based games, however. There are many open-ended board games, where you must think creatively and strategically to win – popular modern examples include *Settlers of Catan®*, *Carcasonne®*, *Ticket to Ride®* and *Pandemic®*, but if you want something a bit more old-school then you could also consider classic board games such as chess, draughts, go and many others.

Using your tangram pieces, and remembering not to flip any of them over, see if you can work out how to make each of the following shapes:

56. Boat

57. House

In addition to the suggestions at the top of the previous page, can you also make pictures that look like the following:

58. A chair

59. A dog

60. Use your creative imagination to visualize what would happen if you were to combine these two grids. The white squares in one should be replaced with the content squares from the other to form a complete picture.

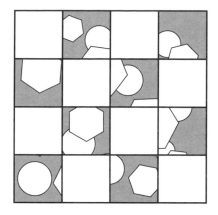 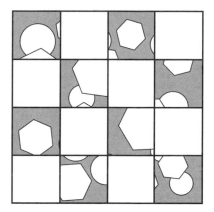

Now answer these questions about the combined image:

- How many hexagons are there?

- How many circles are partially overlapped by hexagons?

- How many circles do not overlap with any other shape?

61. Can you find all six differences between these two images? They are rotated to make it more of a challenge.

QUALITY COMMUNICATION

Learning to express yourself clearly and compactly is useful not just in terms of coming across well when speaking to others, but it also helps you to think with greater clarity. If you are able to represent concepts with fewer words, then you may be better able to manage thoughts related to those concepts in your head – there is less to remember, meaning you can hold more in your memory as you think things through.

Building a good vocabulary is a lifelong task, as well as indeed hopefully a pleasure, and working towards this can be as simple as reading widely. Any reading is probably good for you, but if you are able to read more broadly than a single genre then it's likely to be even *better* for you. Your brain likes to be exposed to new concepts and new situations, and also you are more likely to encounter a wider range of vocabulary.

Another great tip is to do a good crossword puzzle regularly. The 'quick' puzzle from the back page of a daily newspaper is a good start – 'quick' simply means that it is a synonym-based puzzle, rather than the more elaborate cryptic crossword found elsewhere in British newspapers. These are also a good thing to try, but require somewhat more persistence to get started with, since the structure of the various clue types they employ takes time to learn. So 'quick', synonym-based crosswords are great for building vocabulary, although it stands to reason that to learn any new words that are placed in the *grid*, as opposed to the clues, that you will need to check the solutions – or use a crossword solver tool.

VOCABULARY PUZZLES

Start with this 'quick' crossword puzzle, then try the vocabulary puzzles that follow.

62.

Across
1 Plans, as in a course (6)
4 Burrowing marsupial (6)
9 Providing facts (9)
10 Birth name (3)
11 Internet address (inits) (3)
12 Servant (9)
13 Biblical priests' garment (5)
15 Waste from a carcass (5)
20 Long, stringy pasta (9)
22 Become deceased (3)
23 Aardvark's dinner (3)
24 Is more significant than (9)
25 Forgive (6)
26 'Finally!' (2,4)

Down
1 Coterie (6)
2 Really terrible (5)
3 Whirlwind (7)
5 Type of keyboard instrument (5)
6 Fabric square worn around the neck (7)
7 Result of a negotiation (6)
8 Little song (5)
14 Artificial; unnatural (7)
16 Most beautiful (7)
17 Elude (6)
18 Declare (5)
19 One-room apartment (6)
21 Head coverings (5)
22 Doctrine (5)

How many words of three or more letters can you find in each of these word circles? Each word must use the centre letter, plus two or more of the other letters. No letter can be used more than once in a single word. Each has one nine-letter word to find.

63.

H K M
L A L
S R A

_____
_____
_____
_____

64.

N N I
C O T
S N E

_____
_____
_____
_____

65.

S R A
N E U
M R D

_____
_____
_____
_____

66.

A D Q
U O S
N S R

_____
_____
_____
_____

Can you find the 16-letter word hidden in each of these word rectangles? Find words by moving horizontally or vertically from letter to touching letter, but not diagonally, and without revisiting a square in a single word. Also, how many other words of three or more letters can you find?

67.

O	N	T	L
C	N	I	A
S	E	N	T
N	A	R	T

70.

O	G	R	A
I	B	H	P
T	O	I	C
U	A	L	A

68.

T	N	I	S
E	R	O	N
O	C	I	T
N	N	E	C

71.

N	O	I	T
A	L	E	U
I	I	Z	T
N	S	T	I

69.

T	I	E	S
I	L	I	B
S	E	R	I
P	O	N	S

72.

O	N	A	L
I	M	S	I
T	I	N	T
A	N	R	E

ON THE TIP OF YOUR TONGUE

How often have you struggled to remember a word, or the name of a person or place? You often feel as if you can *almost* remember it, and sometimes you are even sure you know the first letter.

In fact, the first letter of a word is a critically important part of our ability to identify it, so when we think we can remember a first letter but no more then there's a good chance we are actually correct. In this respect your brain is very much like the alphabetic index in a book, where words are stored under their initial letter.

So strong is this connection that even when the letters of a word are jumbled, it is often still relatively easy to read so long as the first and last letters remain in the same position, and the words aren't too long. For example, can you read the following phrase?

Tihs sowhs taht it wrkos

It reads 'This shows that it works.' The effect is not quite as remarkable as it is sometimes claimed, however, for when the words get longer it becomes much harder to read them:

Smoe sldpdileny csniunogf wdsro

This reads 'Some splendidly confusing words.' Nonetheless, anagrams are much easier to solve, and words are easier to think of, when we know the first letter. Regular crossword solvers will already be familiar with this.

THE POWER OF WORDS

Words, especially names, carry considerable meaning for us. If we know someone with a particular name and then meet a new person with the same name, our brains will associate some of the characteristics of the existing person with the new person – *based solely on their matching name*. Rationally, of course, we know that this doesn't make any real sense. Despite this, so heavily loaded is the label for that person in our head that when we hear the same label again we recall some of what we have previously learned for the existing person.

Words in turn sometimes have subtle, or perhaps not-so-subtle, variations in meaning to different people, based on our prior experiences – where we grew up, who we spend time with, what films or books we are exposed to, our educational background and so on. Indeed, we all effectively have our own individual private language, since the vocabulary of one person will rarely exactly match that of another, and even if it did then what one person understood by many words would still differ in some respects from what another person understood by them. This is why it's important to always be as clear and explicit as we can when writing or speaking about particularly important matters. Implications that may seem obvious to us may be very *non*-obvious to others. This need to be precise is one reason why many lawyers have their jobs, although it could be argued that many times legal language is so overly precise that it becomes almost impossible for a lay reader to understand what it *really* says!

VOCABULARY SIZE

The single-volume *Oxford Dictionary of English* contains over 350,000 word and phrase definitions. Even if you accept the upper bound of published estimates, which is that a well-educated college graduate might be able to recognize around 60,000 different words, that still leaves a lot of words that most of us won't be familiar with. While it may not always be useful to know many of these words, being exposed to them can help enrich our brains with new concepts in the same way that learning a foreign language can. Online sites such as OED.com and dictionary.com provide 'word of the day' features to help you learn new words, or find out more about words you already know.

VOCABULARY POWER PUZZLES

Use the power of your vocabulary to solve each of these challenges.

Every other letter has been deleted from each of the following sports. How quickly can you find them all?

73. _E_N_S

74. _O_T_A_L

75. _U_B_

76. S_I_M_N_

77. _A_K_T_A_L

78. _O_K_Y

79. _A_M_N_O_

Now try these colours:

80. _U_P_E

81. _R_N_E

82. T_R_U_I_E

83. _O_P_R

84. _H_T_

85. C_I_S_N

86. R_B_

All of the vowels have been deleted from the following films, and then the spacing changed. Can you find all the original titles?

87. FG HTC LB

88. NC PTN

89. CSB LN CA

90. N TRS TL LR

91. MM NT

92. WLL

93. DHR D

94. NS DT

The same letter has been deleted from the start and end of each of these words. Can you recover all the original words?

95. _OPCOA_

96. _RMAD_

97. _YNI_

98. _MOEB_

99. _EURO_

100. _ULA_

101. _AU_

Each of the following letter jumbles can be anagrammed to reveal the name of a country of the world. How many of them can you solve?

102. MEG RYAN

103. THIN AS A FANG

104. AGE GIRO

105. MR NAKED

106. A GREAT INN

107. ARC IGUANA

108. THANK AZ ASK

109. MAD CAR SAGA

Now try the same with these US states:

110. IF A LORD

111. OZ IN AIR

112. CHEATS AS MUSTS

113. WE MIX ONCE

114. SEEN TENSE

115. A LOUTISH ACORN

116. ON HIS LADDER

Given just the initial letters of each of the following classic novels, as well as their authors, can you work out which book each line corresponds to?

117. R C by D D

118. T J by H F

119. E by J A

120. T C O M C by A D

121. D C by C D

122. J E by C B

123. V F by W M T

124. A A I W by L C

Each of the following letter sequences corresponds to a real-world sequence, so for example M T W T F would correspond to Monday, Tuesday, Wednesday, Thursday, Friday. Can you explain all of the following sequences too?

125. F S T F F S

126. A M J J A S

127. M V E M J S

128. H T Q F S S

129. H H L B B C

REASONING WITH LANGUAGE

How do you think? No, really, how *do* you think? When you're trying to explicitly puzzle something out, you talk to yourself with a silent inner monologue, which you use to form your conscious thoughts. Even when the conclusions we reach come to us via a mechanism that we are not consciously aware of, we still think about them in words. So while language may exist as a learned layer on *top* of our ability to reason, it is certainly at the very *core* of our conscious awareness of it.

It's good, therefore, to try word-based games and puzzles where we build our language-based reasoning skills, since our ability to make broad and good use of our vocabulary is so key to our conscious reason.

LANGUAGE REASONING PUZZLES
What connects all four words in each of the following lists?

130. Rite, Right, Write, Wright

131. Parse, Spear, Pears, Spare

132. Madam, Racecar, Kayak, Noon

133. Gouge, False, Eighth, Orange

134. Spy, Rhythm, Lynx, Tryst

Based on your general knowledge, what connects all four items in each of the following lists?

135. Mike, Oscar, Kilo, Hotel

136. Body, Hinting, Finial, Point

137. Powder, Electric, Cambridge, Sky

138. Nonsense, Noisy, Mean, Bounce

139. Blade, Oyster, Skirt, Chuck

140. Caesar, Alberti, Substitution, Hill

141. Nancy, Roger, Susan, John

142. Barron, Eric, Tiffany, Donald

143. Inky, Pinky, Blinky, Clyde

144. West, Clooney, Arnett, Bale

145. Loot, Pyjamas, Avatar, Dinghy

146. Utah, Gold, Sword, Juno

147. Green, Drive, Suspender, Seat

148. Buckeye, Mesa, Glendale, Phoenix

149. Dust, Oversight, Sanction, Clip

150. Snowden, Ritchie, Butler, Jenkins

151. Books, Maps, Play, Santa Tracker

MATHS IS FOR LIFE

Numbers are all around us, from store prices through to recipe quantities, arrival times, currency comparisons and so on. Despite this, there are many who claim that they 'can't do maths', when in fact the truth is usually that they could do it perfectly well if they really wanted to. Many people associate maths with distant memories of school tests, but in reality day-to-day maths requires only basic skills that we all have.

MENTAL ARITHMETIC

When you first try to do sums 'in your head' it can feel a bit stressful. You need to remember both the numbers you're working with *and* the result so far, plus perhaps some partial results too. We make such poor conscious use of our memories that this process of marshalling multiple values can be surprisingly challenging. But what's perhaps even more surprising is that this really does start to get a lot easier with a surprisingly small amount of practice.

When you're out and about, keep a rough reckoning of the amount you're spending in a shop. Don't try to add up every penny, but just try to have a rough idea – and then see how close you were when you check out.

You can challenge yourself in all kinds of other ways too. When you see a date of birth written down, work out how old the person is – although maybe keep the result to yourself! When you have a deadline, work out how many days away it is. And next time you pay with cash, have an idea of how much change you expect.

MULTIPLICATION

Children learn – or are supposed to learn – their 'times tables', so they can rapidly multiply numbers without conscious thought. The problem is that most of us never fully learned those tables, so many people can't instantly tell you the answer to 6 × 7. Being able to rapidly multiply is such a useful skill that it's entirely worth sitting down to try to memorize those sections you missed learning as a kid, if there any.

Multiplication is for example necessary every time you buy more than one of an item and want to have an idea what you're spending. Its close counterpart, division, is essential when working out the effect of a percentage discount, or the per-item or unit price of something bought in bulk. Without these skills we face so many parts of life at a disadvantage.

There are many tricks that can be learned to make multiplication easier, and division has its tricks too – for example, you can find out if a number is divisible by three simply by summing its digits. If these are a multiple of three, then so is the original number. And if it's a multiple of three *and* even, then it is a multiple of six.

NATURAL TALENTS

Take a handful of raisins or nuts, or even cards or pebbles, and sprinkle them over a surface. Divide them into two sections with a sweep of your hand, then quickly look at both sides. The chances are that you will have a good idea which side has the most items. Count and check – you're probably right. Your brain has a natural ability to rapidly compare quantities of items, which was useful on an evolutionary timescale to allow it to rapidly pick the lesser of two threats. With a bit of practice, your brain can extend this ability to a 'feel' for whether one calculated quantity is likely to be higher or lower than another – although this works best when they aren't too close in value.

Take several scraps of paper and write a number on each one. Then randomly place them into two piles and quickly flick through and estimate which pile has the highest sum. Were you correct? Even if you weren't, with a bit of practice you will become much better at this task. If you envisage each number as a weight, and then imagine comparing the weight of each pile, this can help.

MENTAL ARITHMETIC PUZZLES

Solve all of the following mental arithmetic puzzles without making any written notes – that is, just in your head.

For each of the following brain chains, follow each step from the given number until you calculate the final result.

152.

| 31 | +14 | -29 | ×1/2 | ÷4 | +21 | RESULT |

153.

| 43 | -18 | √ | +50 | -35 | +50% | RESULT |

154.

| 24 | ÷6 | ×7 | +25% | -23 | +50% | RESULT |

155.

| 20 | -1 | ×2 | +43 | ×2/3 | ÷9 | RESULT |

156.

| 26 | -50% | +28 | ×2 | +17 | ×1/3 | RESULT |

157.

| 34 | ×1/2 | +58 | -52 | ×4 | -6 | RESULT |

158.

| 20 | ×5 | -29 | +13 | -50% | +22 | RESULT |

159.

| 60 | -34 | +104 | -42 | ×1/4 | +50% | RESULT |

160.

| 67 | -36 | +161 | -75% | ×7/8 | +50% | RESULT |

161.

| 110 | -60% | ×1/2 | +50% | ×2 | -3 | RESULT |

Can you hit every one of the totals given below each number dartboard? Choose one number from each of the three rings of the dartboard so that they sum to one of the given numbers. Each dartboard has three separate totals to try to reach. There is only one way to form each total.

162.

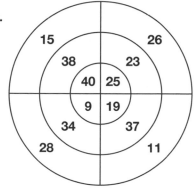

Totals: 63 75 84

164.

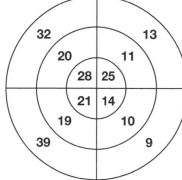

Totals: 52 66 76

163.

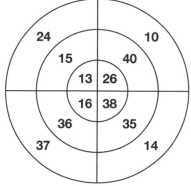

Totals: 61 70 78

165.

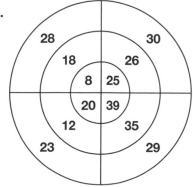

Totals: 57 68 76

ESTIMATING NUMBERS

In most real-life situations you only really need to know the approximate result of a maths calculation, whether it's to check that a discount price is a good deal or to make sure you aren't getting conned in a financial deal.

The great advantage of estimating a number, rather than calculating it exactly, is that if we do it smartly then we can get to our answer much faster than we could via a more precise series of calculations.

ADDING UP A LIST OF NUMBERS

When you're expecting the receipt in a restaurant, you might want to have an idea of what you're likely to owe before it arrives. In situations like this, where you no longer have the exact prices from the menu, your brain will estimate for you without you even consciously asking it to. You'll remember that the side dish cost about £5, and the starter was around £6, without worrying about the exact prices. And in your memory of the menu you will probably round down prices ending in a number less than 50p, and round up those ending in a number greater than 50p. Congratulations, you are using a great technique to estimate the total!

You can consciously use an estimation technique to add up a long list of numbers too, such as a store till receipt. Add up only the amounts in pounds on the list, and apply a few simple rules to the pence:

- If the amount is very close to the next whole number of pounds – for example, ending in .95 or similar – then round up the number of pounds, so £11.95 becomes £12.

- If the amount is very close to the previous whole number of pounds, such as ending in .07 or similar, then round down the number of pounds, so £23.07 becomes £23.

- For all other amounts, keep a rough tally in your head of the total of the pence, and when you feel it has added up to around 100p, add £1 to your mental tally of the number of pounds. It's important that you don't actually *add up* the pence, because this will make the maths much harder – you can consider them as a mental jar of coins that fills up as you throw the spare pence in, and then when you think it's about to overflow you empty it, claim the pound, and start again.

It might take a little practice before you can estimate the total of numbers in this way without too much conscious thought about the pence, but once you can it is sure to prove really useful. The same basic method works whether you are adding or subtracting, too.

RAPID COUNTING

On page 67 we talked about visually comparing two item counts, to decide at a glance which was the most numerous. This also works for estimating actual quantities too, so long as items are not *too* numerous – or partially hidden from vision, such as in a container or in a pile.

Take a handful of small objects of your choice, and drop them on a surface. Small food items, such as nuts or seeds, are one possible option. Spread them out, if necessary, and make a quick estimate of how many there are. Then split them quickly into groups of roughly five or ten items each, and see if you still agree with your estimate. Then you could go ahead and count the exact number, if feasible, but the chances are you can already see you weren't too far from the right total.

As you have just demonstrated, your brain has some impressive built-in reckoning skills when it comes to numbers and quantities, and the more you practise using them the better you will become.

NUMBER CHALLENGES

166. Estimate the result of 8 × 7 × 6 × 5 × 4 × 3 × 2 × 1

167. Now estimate the result of 1 × 2 × 3 × 4 × 5 × 6 × 7 × 8

168. The previous two calculations should of course give the same result, but did you feel that the value of the first product should be higher, because it started with a higher number? Now estimate
19 × 11 × 18 × 12 × 17 × 13 × 16 × 14 × 15

In each of the following puzzles, see how quickly you can spot which of the numbers in the given list can be selected to add up to the totals below. For example, given 2 5 8 9 you could achieve a total of 14 by choosing 5 and 9; or form 19 using 2, 8 and 9.

169.   **22   10   19   25   9   21   7**

Totals to form: 34   55   68   92

170.   **9   23   17   6   25   22   18**

Totals to form: 35   52   77   85

171.   **20   12   25   21   16   24   22**

Totals to form: 40   60   80   100

172. By using all of the given mathematical operators, and all of the numbers, can you form both of the given totals for each set?

7   3   6   4   8   +   +   -   ×

Results to obtain: 82   47

173.

9   10   3   8   5   +   -   ×   ×

Results to obtain: 97   441

Complete these number pyramids by filling in all of the empty bricks. Each brick should contain a total equal to the sum of the two bricks immediately beneath it.

174.

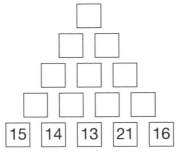

176.

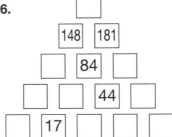

175.

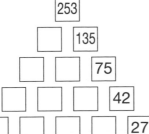

177.

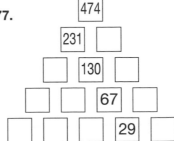

PROBABILITY

Humans have some great innate number skills – but our ability to estimate probabilities is not one of them. Very often we overestimate the likelihood of success, and very much underestimate the probability of failure. It's possible that without this trait we'd be too scared to do or try anything, so it's not necessarily a failing – but when it comes to the numbers game, our instincts aren't always correct.

An inability to grasp the intricacies of probability is one reason why casinos exist. If we properly understood our chances of winning on many of the games then there'd be no takers at all. Even on a simple game like roulette, it's human nature to discount the seemingly 'very unlikely' bank-wins slots, marked '0', and sometimes also '00', on the roulette wheel, and think of all the red/black, odds/even and other two-way bets as being a 50:50 chance. But those 'very unlikely' slots will on average appear 1 in 37 times, or 1 in 19 times in a double-zero casino, meaning that the casino typically retains *all* of the bets on those spins. On the rest it will, on average, break even. Clearly, then, the players betting on the wheel can't also win – if they spin enough times, *every* player will eventually lose all of their money; it's just maths. But it's maths that most people find hard to grasp.

COIN TOSSES AND DICE ROLLS

If you toss a coin then there's a 50:50 chance of either heads or tails, ignoring the extremely unlikely chance that it ends up on its narrow-edged side. So what is the likelihood of tossing heads eight times in a row? It doesn't seem that unlikely, but the actual odds are 1 in $2 \times 2 \times 2 \times 2 \times 2 \times 2 \times 2 \times 2 = 1$ in 256. That's because the probabilities of sequential events *multiply* together. If I was rolling a 6-sided dice, the probability of six '3's in a row, which doesn't seem *too* unlikely at a guess, is actually 1 in $6 \times 6 \times$

$6 \times 6 \times 6 \times 6 = 1$ in 46,656. That's probably far less likely than you would guess!

THE MONTY HALL PROBLEM

Written probability puzzles can be extremely confusing, because they often go against our natural intuition. To be fair, this is sometimes because the question is asked in a way that is contrary to your natural expectations, but even when the question is very simple our innate expectations are often confounded.

In the 'Monty Hall Problem', there is a game show host and there are three closed doors. Between one of the doors is a luxury car, and behind the other two is nothing. The host – and this is key to note – *knows which door the car is behind*.

You are a contestant, and you are asked to choose one of the three doors. You do this at random, so you have a 1 in 3 chance of winning. The host then opens one of the two doors that you didn't choose that he *knows* does not conceal the car. Do you now switch doors, to the closed door you *didn't* pick, or do you stick with the original door – or does it not matter?

Intuitively, most people who encounter this problem think it either doesn't matter, or they say they would prefer to stick with their original choice. They assume that the likelihood of either closed door winning is now 1 in 2, since there are two closed doors and either could win.

But this is a mistake. It's true that if you *started* the game with two closed doors, there'd be a 1 in 2 chance of either, but this is *not* what happened.

PROBABILITY PUZZLES

178. Should you switch doors in the situation described in the Monty Hall Problem, above, or does it not matter? What are the odds of winning in either case?

179. In a particular country the rulers decide that they want there to be fewer boys than girls in the country, so they come up with the following rule:

Each couple can keep having children while they continue to have girls, but as soon as they have a boy they can no longer have any further children.

The rulers assume that this rule will mean there will soon be many more girls, since families can have as many girls as they want, but no more than one boy. Are they correct?

180. In a different country, a couple have five sons, and each son has a sister. How many children do they have overall?

181. In yet another country, there is a father who has two children, at least one of whom is a girl. You don't know the gender of the other child, but given what you *do* know then what is the probability that the father has two girls? Just to clarify, you're not being asked the probability of *a* father having two girls, but rather the chance that *this* father has two girls, *given what you already know*.

182. A couple, Andrea and Bob, host a party and invite four other couples. Each person on arrival gives a business card to every other person they haven't met before.

Andrea notices that all eight people out of the four couples attending, as well as Bob, has received a different number of business cards to each other.

How many business cards does Bob now have?

183. At a roulette wheel with numbers 1 to 36 plus a single 0 for the bank, what is the likelihood that I will win if I place chips on every multiple of five on the board?

184. If I roll five six-sided dice, what is the likelihood that I roll five identical numbers?

185. If I toss a coin eight times, how likely am I to have all tails or all heads?

186. If the likelihood of winning the lottery is one in ten, and I play twice this year, how likely am I to win this year?

187. Now test your maths *and* logic skills with this calcudoku puzzle. Place the numbers 1 to 6 once each into every row and column of each grid, while obeying the region clues.

The value at the top left of each bold-lined region must be obtained when all of the numbers in that region have the given operation (+, -, ×, ÷) applied between them. For - and ÷ operations, begin with the largest number in the region and then subtract or divide by the other numbers in the region in any order.

24×			15+		2−
12×		6+			
10×	3×	3−		2÷	20×
		24×			
4×	12+	8×		3−	
			10+		

CONSIDER THE EVIDENCE

You don't require any special genius to be able to think logically. Simply take note of what you're looking at, or considering, then take the time to think it through. Maybe describe it to yourself and then draw some preliminary conclusions. Look for connections between parts – if one thing changes does it influence anything else? If that influence isn't what I want, what could I do differently?

Take what you know for sure and call it 'evidence', and see if you can come up with a theory that explains that evidence. Do the facts fit it? What about other, related events? Can the same theory work there too? If not, why not, and what can be done to amend it?

In life in general, a good theory will work over many events, and be able to successfully predict outcomes for events *not* known about when creating the theory. The test of any theory is not how well it works on the information used to create the theory, since it is always possible to find a theory to explain known data, but to see if it works for any previously unknown data. Politicians and others in public view frequently make predictions based on very limited past data, or even mere supposition, without any rigorous logical analysis of what has gone before. There is also a tendency to cherry-pick facts, which at a single stroke will instantly invalidate any conclusions drawn from those facts.

SAFETY IN NUMBERS
Spending just a few moments thinking about the real meaning of information can be extremely helpful. For example, it is very common

to read in the press about a so-called 'scientific' study which looks at the impact of a medical treatment on a few dozen people. Before you even consider the many ways it is possible for these studies to be flawed, the fact is that such numbers are generally too small to draw firm conclusions – the results could be simply down to chance. What's more, not all studies are reported in the press so we are making things worse by selecting the 'interesting' outliers, which typically means the most sensational ones.

Imagine I toss a coin ten times and get five heads and five tails, but then I drop it instead and get eight heads and two tails. I *could* then conclude that this method makes me more likely to get heads, but because I have taken very few samples my *confidence* should be relatively low. In this instance, we happen to know for sure that if we took a much larger sample set the apparent benefit of dropping would turn out to have been an illusion.

It's this 'confidence', or statistical significance to give it another name, that should be used to judge any data-based analysis. Our human brains love finding patterns, so we lend them greater credence than they deserve.

FUZZY CONCLUSIONS

Although firm conclusions may not be able to be reached from small sample sizes, this doesn't always mean that nothing useful can be gained. Particularly when considering our own day-to-day lives, the sum of our experience to date often provides a solid grounding for considering specific events, even if we don't consciously evaluate them in that way.

For example, why did the person you were talking to get upset? You have no way of being certain, and perhaps they were just having a bad day, but what was the trigger? Has that trigger ever caused the same effect before? And why didn't the car salesman give you a discount? Was it already discounted, or did you appear too keen to buy? It's sometimes worth taking a moment to analyse an event, but not to *over*-analyse or worry about what happened – remember that you need a huge amount of data to start to reach any firm conclusions! People act randomly outside of our control, and their behaviours can have many possible explanations.

LOGICAL IMPLICATIONS

How do you go about solving a sudoku, or any other logic-based puzzle? Sudoku is a particularly simple puzzle, but despite this simplicity it can still require complex logic to solve. With more complex puzzles, the logic can be even more involved.

Logical reasoning can be presented as a successive series of 'what if' questions. In a sudoku puzzle, if I don't place a 1 in this square then is there anywhere else in this row/column/box it can go? Or, perhaps, if I don't place a 1 in this square, is there any other number that can fit in this square? These may seem similar steps, but they are typically very different to apply – scanning a region for a missing number is fairly straightforward, but spotting that there is a square where *only* one number can fit is much harder! But nonetheless, coming up with these strategies in the first place is an important part of solving the puzzle.

Well-designed logic puzzles are usually crafted so that you can make each successive deduction by careful observation of the puzzle, without requiring any guesses. An experimental guess, however, that can be undone if it proves to be wrong, is still a perfectly valid logical step. If I place this here and carry on solving, is the puzzle still possible or do I reach a contradiction? If I reach a contradiction, I undo all of the deductions from the guess onwards, and try a different option. Sensible choices of place to guess mean that, even when you reach a contradiction, you learn something else useful. Guessing in this way can work well with a heavily constrained puzzle, such as a sudoku, especially if you have narrowed a square down to two options in an almost-complete puzzle.

Especially if a puzzle is nearly complete, it may well be that guessing and looking for a contradiction is the fastest way to finish it. If you don't find one quickly, however, it may be best to stop exploring that particular option and try another.

PROVING A CONTRADICTION

If you feel fairly sure a particular deduction is *false* then it can be useful to pretend it is *true* and then look for a resulting contradiction. Sometimes the inverse of an option is much easier to analyse than its positive version. This same advice can be applied to many situations. Thinking about the opposite of a situation can often be very informative. What are the reasons for doing something, but also what are the reasons for *not* doing it?

PATTERN SPOTTING

The longer you spend on many types of puzzle, the more you learn to spot patterns in those puzzles. You may even spot patterns based on the way the puzzles are set – for example, there may be certain clue arrangements in a logic puzzle that recur time and again. Once you have learned to make sense of these patterns the first time, you know to apply similar logic in future. It's the same general method your brain uses in day-to-day life, whereby your experience with tackling life's many real-world challenges allows you to better handle similar tasks in the future.

The more you solve different types of puzzle, the better you will get at finding logic that can help you make progress as your brain learns to ask more and more sensible 'what if' questions earlier in the solving process. You'll also get better at considering the options in your head, such as the way that skilled sudoku players can 'see' at a glance which numbers are missing from a region, without having to run through them one by one.

You'll also find general rules that can be applied across multiple puzzles – for example, in any loop puzzle, such as the one at the top of the following page, there must always be an *even* number of loop segments travelling in and out of an area, so if a move will make that impossible then it must be wrong. If not, there would be a part of the loop that couldn't connect.

LOGIC PUZZLES

188. Draw a single loop by connecting some dots with horizontal and vertical lines, so that each numbered square has the specified number of adjacent line segments. The loop cannot cross or touch itself.

```
  2     2     1           3

  2                 3     2

1     3     2     3 2     3

  0     2                 0     2

  2 2           2     3

      3     0           1 1

2     2                 0     1

2     3 3     0     0     3

  3     1                 1

2           3     1     1
```

189. Join dots with horizontal and vertical lines to form a single path which does not touch or cross itself, or any of the solid blocks, at any point. The start and end of the path are given. Numbers outside the grid specify the exact number of dots in their row or column that are visited by the path.

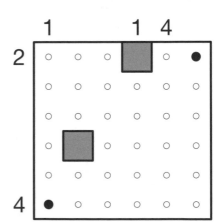

190. Place A to G once each into every row, column and bold-lined region.

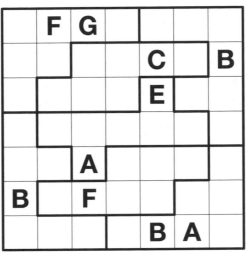

191. Draw a horizontal or vertical line across the full width or height of each empty square. Numbers on shaded squares reveal the total length of all lines touching them, measured in square lengths.

192. Write a number into each of the empty squares, so that the grid contains every number from 1 to 81 exactly once. Place the numbers so that there is a route from 1 to 81 that visits every grid square exactly once in increasing numerical order, moving only left, right, up or down – but not diagonally – between touching squares.

	23						53	
		25				49		
			35		47			
			39		59			
		17				61		
	15						63	

193. Place 1 to 5 once each into every row and column of this grid. Place digits in the grid in such a way that each given clue number outside the grid represents the number of digits that are 'visible' from that point, looking along that clue's row or column.

A digit is visible unless there is a higher digit preceding it, reading in order along that row or column. For example, if a row was '21435' then the 2, 4 and 5 would be visible (giving a clue of '3' visible digits), since 1 is obscured by the preceding higher 2, and 3 is obscured by the preceding higher 4.

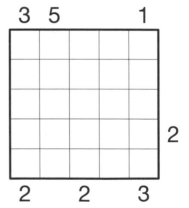

194. Join circled numbers with horizontal or vertical lines. Each number must have as many lines connected to it as specified by its value. No more than two lines may join any pair of numbers, and no lines may cross. The finished layout must connect all numbers, so you can travel between any pair of numbers by following one or more lines.

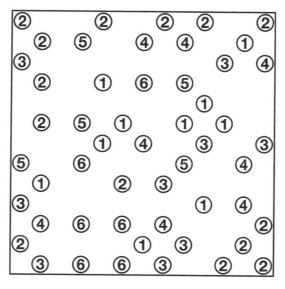

195. Place the letters A, B and C exactly once each into every row and column of squares inside the grid. Two squares in each row or column will therefore be empty. Letters outside the grid indicate which letter appears closest to that end in the clue's row or column.

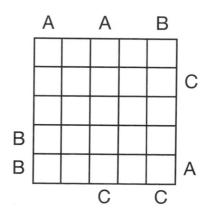

196. Place 1 to 7 once each into every row and column while obeying the inequality signs. Greater than (>) signs between some squares indicate that the value in one square is greater than that in another as indicated by the sign. The sign always points towards the smaller number.

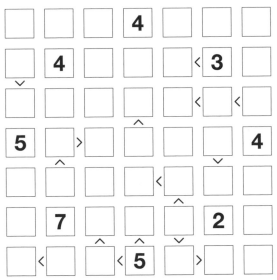

197. Place 1 to 6 once each into every row and column of the grid. Some intersections contain 4 digits, which are to be placed into the touching 4 squares in some order.

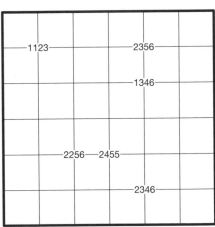

198. Place a digit from 1 to 9 into each white square. Each horizontal run of white squares adds up to the total above the diagonal line to the left of the run, and each vertical run of white squares adds up to the total below the diagonal line above the run. No digit can be used more than once in any run.

199. Draw a single loop through some empty squares, made up of horizontal and vertical lines between square centres. The loop does not cross or overlap itself, and can only pass through empty grid squares. Squares with numbers indicate how many touching squares the loop passes through, including diagonally touching squares.

WORKING BACKWARDS

It's often instructive, when tackling new types of puzzle, to try deconstructing a solution. A well-designed logic puzzle will have only one unique solution. If it didn't then there would always be a point in the solution where you *had* to guess, since multiple options would be equally valid and there would be no reason to choose between them. When it comes to printed puzzles this is generally considered unfair, and in a book it would mean that the solution at the back wouldn't always match your own solution. All of the logic puzzles in this book have unique solutions.

BEING AT THE END

In day-to-day life you don't have the luxury of beginning at the end, but with a printed puzzle you do. Look at the solution and consider the various given clues, and experiment to see what would happen if the clue wasn't there. Would there be an alternative solution, and if so what might that be? Not all clues are necessarily needed in logic puzzles, however, since they may be there for visual balance – such as a pleasing clue symmetry in a sudoku – or in order to make the puzzle easier to solve. But even so, it's often instructive to examine a solution and see how the various components fit together, and what has resulted from each clue. This is particularly true for more complex puzzles, where the connection between a given clue and its effect may be less directly obvious.

Another use for a solution is to create an easier puzzle. Keep adding parts of the solution to the puzzle until you are able to make a new deduction. You can also use them to check your solve as you go, and perhaps alert you to false assumptions you didn't realize you had made. Especially when learning to solve new puzzles, there's nothing wrong with getting a helping hand in this way. You could try it with some of the puzzles on the following pages, if you wish.

COUNTER-INTUITIVE STEPS

Sometimes the solution to a puzzle requires a counter-intuitive step. In the classic fox, goose and grain puzzle, you must escort all three across a river using a single boat. Unfortunately only two will fit in the boat at any one time, and if you leave the fox alone with the goose it will kill it, or if you leave the goose alone with the grain it will eat it. So how do you cross the river? Can you work it out?

The reason this puzzle is often found hard to solve is that solving it requires you to *reverse* a step you have already made. You must bring one of the three across the river with you, and then bring it *back* too. Reversing a step we have already made seems counter-intuitive.

The solution is to cross with the fox and goose (or goose and grain), then leave the goose on the opposite side *but return with the other* (the fox or the grain). Then you can pick up the remaining item and return to the far side.

SMART REASONING PUZZLES

Try this puzzle, which works in a similar way.

200. Four tourists reach a rickety old bridge late at night, which they need to cross to get to their hotel. They only have one torch between them, but the battery is about to go and so they want to cross the bridge as fast as possible.

Unfortunately, a sign warns them that the bridge can't hold the weight of more than two people at any one time. And they'll need the torch to cross, since it's clearly damaged and they don't want to plunge into the icy waters far below!

The tourists all move at different speeds and will each take a different amount of time to cross the bridge.

(continued overleaf...)

Here's how long each tourist will take to cross the bridge:

- Zeus will take eight minutes to cross

- Yolanda will take five minutes to cross

- Xavier will take two minutes to cross

- Walder will take one minute to cross

When the tourists cross the bridge, they'll always need to have the torch with them and so they'll have to cross at the speed of the slowest person in each pair.

The bridge is too long to be able to throw the torch back to the other side, so each time a pair crosses then one of the pair will have to come back to the original side with the torch.

It turns out that the battery of the torch will last for just 15 minutes – find a strategy that allows all four of the tourists to reach the other side in this exact amount of time.

201. Solve this 'backwards' puzzle where the clues are written outside the grid. Place a single digit from 1 to 6 into every square, so that each digit appears once in every row and column *inside* the grid. Some digits are given outside the grid. These digits must be placed in the nearest two squares in their row or column. If there is one digit, it is up to you to work out which of the two squares to place it into. If there are two digits, they may be placed in either order.

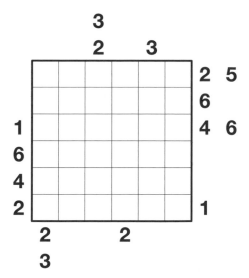

202. In this skeleton crossword most of the grid is missing. Work backwards from the clues to fill in not just the answers but also the grid itself. The grid has rotational symmetry, just like the crossword on page 55, so you can shade in a few squares immediately.

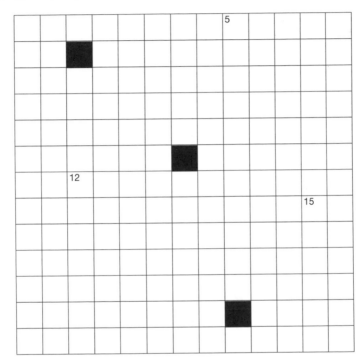

Across

1 Etch (7)
5 Declare (5)
9 Physical convulsion due to the flow of current (8,5)
10 Something that calms (8)
11 Foremost (4)
12 Smoker's need (9)
16 Chinese dynasty (4)
17 Efficient (8)
19 Absolute (13)
21 Age (5)
22 Christmas or Easter (4,3)

Down

2 Neckband (6)
3 Storing records (9)
4 Welsh breed of dog (5)
6 Royal family members (inits) (3)
7 Ploy (6)
8 Meagre; unusual (6)
11 A set of foundation stories (9)
13 Plan (6)
14 Enrol (4,2)
15 Noisy grass insect (6)
18 Exceed (5)
20 Ogre (3)

VISUAL AND SPATIAL AWARENESS

The human brain has the remarkable ability to make easy sense of the visual world around us. We don't usually need to devote much conscious thought to working out what we are looking at, because our brains do it all for us. As babies we learn to recognize objects, shapes and movement, and then as adults these skills are so deeply learned that we rarely give them a moment's thought. Some of our visual learning does have weaknesses, however, and it's good to be aware of them.

PERCEPTION OF SPEED

We aren't very good at judging speeds of objects. Have you ever looked out from a building directly alongside a motorway, such as a service station, and been surprised at just how fast the cars are passing by? And yet when you are in a car on the very same motorway, your perception of speed feels very different. Perhaps if we were all able to sit outside and watch ourselves drive by, there would be fewer dangerous speeding incidents.

When it comes to natural sources of movement, such as someone sprinting or throwing a ball, our judgements are far more accurate. Unfortunately, both our development as a baby – children don't sit by motorways, or learn to drive – and our evolutionary history have not prepared us well for judging high speeds. When driving, most people hugely underestimate how quickly they will reach a vehicle in front should it suddenly brake, nor have any accurate perception of the distance they will require to come to a standstill should they need to brake suddenly. If we come upon a slower vehicle on a fast road, we find ourselves catching up with it much faster than we anticipate – a potentially dangerous lesson that most new drivers experience at some point. The problem is that we don't *know* how bad we are at these judgements, so we consistently overestimate our own abilities.

Perception of speed isn't just important when driving, but also when travelling in any way near objects moving at high speed. Children have even less idea than adults how quickly a vehicle can close on them, so often make very poor judgements in terms of attempting to cross the road, or head out into a road to retrieve a ball, or avoid a barking dog. This is why it's essential to educate about road safety from an early age.

MIRRORS

Although we become familiar with mirrors from an early age, the chances are that you will still need to consciously think whether something is on your right or left when looking at a reflection. Keep in mind, however, that many people have trouble with this concept even when *not* reflected!

Try placing a tray of objects in front of a mirror, and see how well you can pick up and manipulate those objects using just the mirror as your guide. You might be surprised at how tricky this is. It's good to practise using mirrors in complete safety, like this, rather than when driving a car and facing a potentially dangerous situation.

PERCEPTION OF HEIGHTS

We are astonishingly poor at judging heights. If you have ever been to a city with many very tall buildings, such as Manhattan, you will find that if you look upwards from road level that many of the tall buildings all look identical in height. And yet if you climb to the top of a skyscraper such as the Empire State Building, you will be astonished to look down and see just how much they vary in height.

This same weakness exists with much smaller heights too. If you are asked to judge the width and height of a tree, you will typically underestimate the height relative to the width. The taller the item, the greater the disparity between your judgement and the reality.

VISUAL AND SPATIAL AWARENESS PUZZLES

203. Even on a printed page, it can be tricky to judge heights. Looking at the diagram below, make a quick, snap decision on which of the lines on the right is the continuation of the line on the left. Many people get this wrong – use a straight-edged object, such as a ruler, to find out if you were correct.

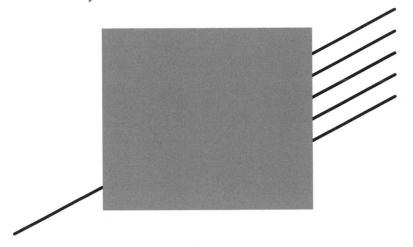

204. Draw borders along the grid lines in this image to divide it into four identical shapes, with no unused squares. The shapes can be rotated relative to one another, but cannot be reflected.

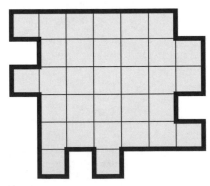

205. Draw exactly three straight lines to divide up this image so that there is exactly one of each size of circle in each resulting area.

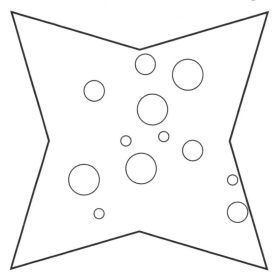

206. Draw exactly three straight lines to divide up this image so that there is exactly one of each type of shape in each resulting area.

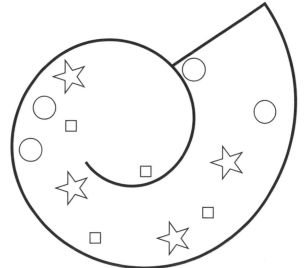

THINKING IN THREE DIMENSIONS

The world around us is constructed in three dimensions, with objects positioned not just left/right or up/down from us, but also with depth near/far from us. However, much of the time information is presented to us on a flat, two-dimensional page or screen – without depth. Being able to readily transform that flat representation into an accurate concept of its three-dimensional representation is therefore a key skill. In some circumstances, such as reading a map when travelling at speed, it can even be critically important.

When it comes to navigating our way from A to B, we are able to do this with relative ease when traveling at walking pace. But as soon as we are moving much faster, as when driving, we need to make more pressurized, quicker decisions. We need to judge the curve and width of a road, as well as the width, length, direction and speed of the vehicle we are driving. Not just this, but the gap between us and the car in front, and the impact of obstacles that we are passing, such as parked cars and traffic coming the other way. At night, we need to infer some of this from even less visual information, and ignore significant distractions such as glare. And when it's raining or misty, there's even more visual confusion. Given all these issues, it's incredible that we are able to manage this process at all, but clearly the faster we travel the less time we are giving ourselves to make corrections should any of these instantaneous calculations be wrong.

Being able to read a map allows us to prepare in advance for some of the decisions we face when driving, or indeed navigating in any way. Learning to understand how our current direction corresponds to what we see on a map, and to translate a series of twists and turns into a rough idea in our head of which direction we should be heading, means that we can be better prepared to handle the road ahead. In many cases map information will be provided dynamically via a GPS-based system, meaning that the ability to immediately interpret the map drawings, or simulated 3D projection on-screen, can be critical to safe driving.

It's useful, therefore, to practise these skills. If you find translating a map into reality tricky, then obtain a map of your local area – or use a smart device with one on and disable auto-rotation – and go outside and walk around until it starts to make more sense. Even if this takes many walks over many weeks, it's a skill well worth learning. Over time you may develop a better sense of direction, allowing you to instinctively know which direction is 'home', at least when walking relatively short distances.

PACKING

Another three-dimensionally based skill is packing, whether it's loading a box for posting or fitting several sets of luggage into a car boot. Some may seem to have an instinctive concept of how things will fit, but in reality it's mostly a mix of experience and common sense. Starting with the largest objects usually works best, and then using small objects to fill gaps around them so as not to waste space. Lots of practice as a child, or indeed adult, with building bricks of various shapes and sizes no doubt helps, but as with many things in life a small pause to think before beginning is often the real key.

THREE-DIMENSIONAL MANIPULATION

Many people find it tricky to imagine rotating three-dimensional objects in their head, especially if rotating them to unusual angles. If you're imagining manipulating the object at the same time as well, for example by folding it, it can even feel mentally overwhelming when you try to picture it. But like many things that seem extremely hard when you first try them, it becomes easier with practice. Most of us lack much direct experience with this kind of deliberate manipulation, so even just a little practice can be surprisingly useful. There are some suitable exercises on the following two pages.

THREE-DIMENSIONAL VISUALIZATION

207. You're holding a spherical object in your hand, such as a football for example, and you mark three points on it at random. What is the chance that all three marks end up all on the same half of the sphere?

208. All but three of the following shape nets could be folded up to form a perfect six-sided cube – which three are the ones that could not?

209. Three of these cube nets will fold up to form identical cubes, but one will be slightly different. Which is the odd one out?

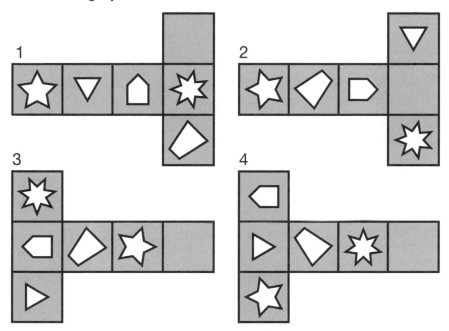

210. Which of the three pyramids below does this shape net make?

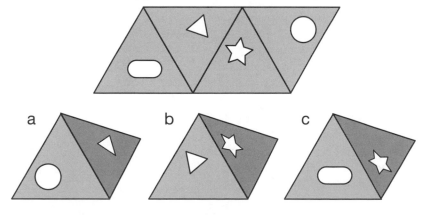

211. Which of the following shape nets could be folded up to make a perfect four-sided triangular-based pyramid?

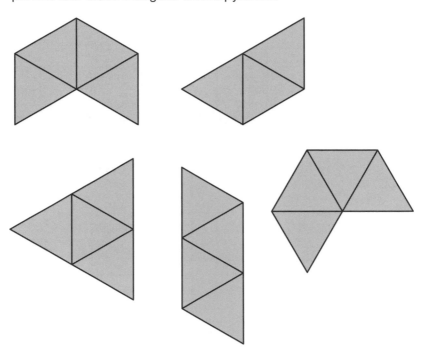

Now imagine that you have a set of cubes arranged as shown to the right. This cuboid is five wide by four deep by four high. Imagine that you remove some cubes. Given that every cube that isn't on the bottom level has to be supported by another and cannot be floating in space, how many cubes are there in each of the following images?

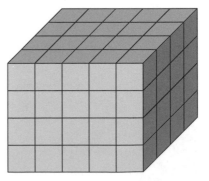

212.

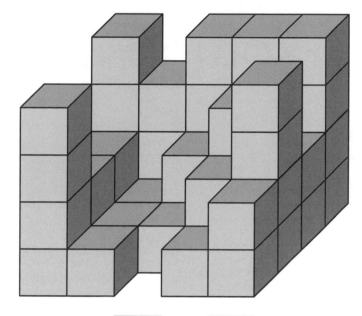

213.

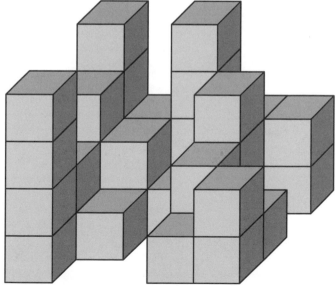

SOLUTIONS

PUZZLE 1

	1	9	5	8	3	6	4	2
6	2	3	7	4		1	8	9
5	4	8	9	6	1		7	3
8	7		3	9	2	5	6	1
2	3	5		7	6	8	9	4
1	9	6	8	5	4	2	3	
9	5	1	4		8	3	2	7
3		2	6	1	7	4	5	8
4	8	7	2	3	5	9		6

PUZZLE 2

O	×	×	O	×	×
×	O	O	×	×	×
×	O	×	O	O	O
×	O	×	O	×	×
O	×	O	×	O	×
×	×	×	O	×	O

PUZZLE 3

1	4	4	1	1	3	0	5
1	3	6	3	3	2	2	6
6	5	0	3	2	3	1	5
6	6	4	1	4	6	0	2
0	2	1	2	2	5	5	0
2	4	3	3	6	4	4	0
1	5	5	4	5	0	6	0

PUZZLE 4

1	1	0	0	1	0	1	0
0	0	1	1	0	0	1	1
1	0	0	1	0	1	0	1
0	1	1	0	1	0	1	0
0	0	1	1	0	1	0	1
1	0	0	1	0	0	1	1
0	1	1	0	1	1	0	0
1	1	0	0	1	1	0	0

PUZZLE 5

Horizontally: 8   Vertically: 10
Total: 18 times

PUZZLE 6

It's the 1st of January today, and my birthday is on the 31st of December

PUZZLE 7

Friday is the name of his horse

PUZZLE 8

Put it down on its side. It will be easy to see if it is half full or not

PUZZLE 9

One way is to get every jockey to swap horses with another

PUZZLE 10

One method is to slowly pour sand into the hole, so the hamster can climb up bit by bit

PUZZLE 11

The match

PUZZLE 12

Fold your arms before you pick up the scarf. When you fold them, make sure that one hand is on top of the other arm, and the other hand is sitting under the remaining arm. Then unfold them.

PUZZLE 13

Put your jeans on backwards or inside out

PUZZLE 14

I live near the poles, where during winter there is no sunrise

PUZZLE 15

They may predict it; they may well not be accurate, however!

PUZZLE 16

One of the fathers was the son of the other

father, who passed on the first heirloom

PUZZLE 17
In a dictionary

PUZZLE 18
Just catch it!

PUZZLE 19
Holes

PUZZLE 20
Half way

PUZZLE 21
White – I'm at the North Pole

PUZZLE 22

PUZZLE 23

PUZZLE 24

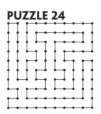

PUZZLE 25

PUZZLE 26

PUZZLE 27

PUZZLE 28
Simply view it in a mirror:

PUZZLE 29

PUZZLE 30

PUZZLE 31

Inward		**Outward**	
1-6	GOLDEN	100-95	BONSAI
7-9	REV	94-89	PESETA
10-14	OGLES	88-84	RISKS
15-18	NITS	83-78	ATTEND
19-22	SENT	77-74	ALAS
23-27	PANEL	73-70	LOCO
28-30	LOP	69-63	TORPEDO
31-37	DESSERT	62-57	REDUCE
38-42	SIDED	56-54	GEL
43-46	ICON	53-49	LATER
47-51	EGRET	48-41	GENOCIDE
52-57	ALLEGE	40-31	DISTRESSED
58-60	CUD	30-25	POLLEN
61-65	ERODE	24-18	APTNESS
66-73	PROTOCOL	17-12	TINSEL
74-78	SALAD	11-4	GOVERNED
79-81	NET	3-1	LOG
82-86	TASKS		
87-91	IRATE		
92-96	SEPIA		
97-100	SNOB		

PUZZLE 32

PUZZLE 33

PUZZLE 34

PUZZLE 35

Poppy, rose, tulip, lily, lavender, peony

PUZZLE 36

11 times

PUZZLE 37

PUZZLE 38

99 of them can definitely survive, and all 100 might with a 50:50 chance. The prisoners at the back can agree that the first prisoner, who can see everyone, calls out 'red' if he sees an odd number of red hats, and 'blue' if he sees an even number of red hats. Now the person in front of him can simply count how many hats he can see – if he is expecting an odd number of red hats but sees an even number, he *knows* he is wearing a red hat since the difference must be accounted for by him. If, however, he is expecting an odd number of red hats and *sees* an odd number of red hats, then he must be wearing blue. The prisoner in front can then update his expectations appropriately – if the guy behind him calls out 'red', he will change his expectation of red hats from odd to even, or from even to odd. If he calls out 'blue', he won't change it. And so on down the line, with all prisoners now able to answer correctly.

PUZZLE 39

11 glasses. He can make 10 glasses initially, then pour the remains of these together to make one more.

PUZZLE 40

The man breaks each pill in half, discarding one half and consuming the other. By the time he is done he will have eaten a total of one green pill and one yellow pill.

PUZZLE 41

Samuel is telling the truth. If Diana was telling the truth she'd contradict herself, and Dave can't be telling the truth since none of the three agree.

PUZZLE 42

Walk in circles around and around the tree, with the dog following as described, until the leash becomes short enough that you can reach the car. The dog would have to race back around to free itself, even if it was smart enough, during which time you could get inside the car.

PUZZLE 43

PUZZLE 44

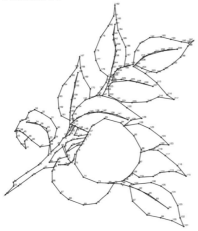

PUZZLE 50

How about 'It was a crazy ant-tic'?!

PUZZLE 51

Maybe 'One is a staple and the other is a stable'?

PUZZLE 52

'It depends on his name', perhaps!

PUZZLE 56

PUZZLE 57

PUZZLE 60

11 hexagons
9 circles
2 non-overlapping circles

PUZZLE 61

PUZZLE 62

PUZZLE 63

Nine-letter word: hallmarks

PUZZLE 64

Nine-letter word: innocents

PUZZLE 65

Nine-letter word: underarms

PUZZLE 66

Nine-letter word: squadrons

PUZZLE 67
Sixteen-letter word: transcontinental

PUZZLE 68
Sixteen-letter word: interconnections

PUZZLE 69
Sixteen-letter word: responsibilities

PUZZLE 70
Sixteen-letter word: autobiographical

PUZZLE 71
Sixteen-letter word: institutionalize

PUZZLE 72
Sixteen-letter word: internationalism

PUZZLE 73
TENNIS

PUZZLE 74
FOOTBALL

PUZZLE 75
RUGBY

PUZZLE 76
SWIMMING

PUZZLE 77
BASKETBALL

PUZZLE 78
HOCKEY

PUZZLE 79
BADMINTON

PUZZLE 80
PURPLE

PUZZLE 81
ORANGE

PUZZLE 82
TURQUOISE

PUZZLE 83
COPPER

PUZZLE 84
WHITE

PUZZLE 85
CRIMSON

PUZZLE 86
RUBY

PUZZLE 87
Fight Club

PUZZLE 88
Inception

PUZZLE 89
Casablanca

PUZZLE 90
Interstellar

PUZZLE 91
Memento

PUZZLE 92
WALL-E

PUZZLE 93
Die Hard

PUZZLE 94
Inside Out

PUZZLE 95
TOPCOAT

PUZZLE 96
ARMADA

PUZZLE 97
CYNIC

PUZZLE 98
AMOEBA

PUZZLE 99
NEURON

PUZZLE 100
GULAG

106

PUZZLE 101
TAUT

PUZZLE 102
Germany

PUZZLE 103
Afghanistan

PUZZLE 104
Georgia

PUZZLE 105
Denmark

PUZZLE 106
Argentina

PUZZLE 107
Nicaragua

PUZZLE 108
Kazakhstan

PUZZLE 109
Madagascar

PUZZLE 110
Florida

PUZZLE 111
Arizona

PUZZLE 112
Massachusetts

PUZZLE 113
New Mexico

PUZZLE 114
Tennessee

PUZZLE 115
South Carolina

PUZZLE 116
Rhode Island

PUZZLE 117
Robinson Crusoe by Daniel Defoe

PUZZLE 118
Tom Jones by Henry Fielding

PUZZLE 119
Emma by Jane Austen

PUZZLE 120
The Count of Monte Cristo by Alexandre Dumas

PUZZLE 121
David Copperfield by Charles Dickens

PUZZLE 122
Jane Eyre by Charlotte Brontë

PUZZLE 123
Vanity Fair by William Makepeace Thackeray

PUZZLE 124
Alice's Adventures In Wonderland by Lewis Carroll

PUZZLE 125
Ordinal numbers: First second third fourth fifth sixth

PUZZLE 126
Months: April May June July August September

PUZZLE 127
Planets: Mercury Venus Earth Mars Jupiter Saturn

PUZZLE 128
Fractions: Half third quarter fifth sixth seventh

PUZZLE 129
Periodic table elements: Hydrogen helium lithium beryllium boron carbon

PUZZLE 130
Homophones

PUZZLE 131
Anagrams of one another

PUZZLE 132
Palindromic words

PUZZLE 133
Words that have no perfect rhymes in English

PUZZLE 134
Vowelless words

PUZZLE 135
Phonetic alphabet letters

PUZZLE 136
Font terms

PUZZLE 137
Blues

PUZZLE 138
Mr. Men

PUZZLE 139
Cuts of beef

PUZZLE 140
Cypher codes

PUZZLE 141
Characters in *Swallows and Amazons*

PUZZLE 142
Donald Trump's children

PUZZLE 143
Pac-Man® ghosts

PUZZLE 144
Batman actors

PUZZLE 145
English words of Indian origin

PUZZLE 146
D-Day landing beaches

PUZZLE 147
Belts

PUZZLE 148
Cities in Arizona

PUZZLE 149
Words that can mean their own opposite

PUZZLE 150
20th century UK Chancellors of the Exchequer

PUZZLE 151
Google products

PUZZLE 152

| 31 | 45 | 16 | 8 | 2 | 23 |

PUZZLE 153

| 43 | 25 | 5 | 55 | 20 | 30 |

PUZZLE 154

| 24 | 4 | 28 | 35 | 12 | 18 |

PUZZLE 155

| 20 | 19 | 38 | 81 | 54 | 6 |

PUZZLE 156

| 26 | 13 | 41 | 82 | 99 | 33 |

PUZZLE 157

| 34 | 17 | 75 | 23 | 92 | 86 |

PUZZLE 158

| 20 | 100 | 71 | 84 | 42 | 64 |

PUZZLE 159

| 60 | 26 | 130 | 88 | 22 | 33 |

PUZZLE 160

| 67 | 31 | 192 | 48 | 42 | 63 |

PUZZLE 161

| 110 | 44 | 22 | 33 | 66 | 63 |

PUZZLE 162
63 = 25 + 23 + 15
75 = 9 + 38 + 28
84 = 19 + 37 + 28

PUZZLE 163
61 = 16 + 35 + 10

70 = 16 + 40 + 14
78 = 26 + 15 + 37

PUZZLE 164
52 = 28 + 11 + 13
66 = 14 + 20 + 32
76 = 25 + 19 + 32

PUZZLE 165
57 = 8 + 26 + 23
68 = 20 + 18 + 30
76 = 20 + 26 + 30

PUZZLE 166
The actual answer is 40,320

PUZZLE 167
The actual answer is 40,320

PUZZLE 168
33,522,128,640

PUZZLE 169
34 = 9 + 25
55 = 9 + 21 + 25
68 = 21 + 22 + 25
92 = 7 + 9 + 10 + 19 + 22 + 25

PUZZLE 170
35 = 17 + 18
52 = 9 + 18 + 25
77 = 6 + 9 + 17 + 22 + 23
85 = 6 + 9 + 22 + 23 + 25

PUZZLE 171
40 = 16 + 24
60 = 16 + 20 + 24
80 = 12 + 21 + 22 + 25
100 = 12 + 20 + 21 + 22 + 25

PUZZLE 172
82 = (7 + 3) × 8 + 6 - 4
47 = (8 + 6 + 4) × 3 - 7

PUZZLE 173
97 = 8 × 9 + (10 × 3) - 5
441 = ((9 + 10) × 8 - 5) × 3

PUZZLE 174

249
117 132
56 61 71
29 27 34 37
15 14 13 21 16

PUZZLE 175

253
118 135
58 60 75
31 27 33 42
22 9 18 15 27

PUZZLE 176

329
148 181
64 84 97
28 40 44 53
11 17 23 21 32

PUZZLE 177

474
231 243
101 130 113
38 63 67 46
13 25 38 29 17

PUZZLE 178
You should *always* switch doors. Whatever happens *after* you make your original choice doesn't change your chance of winning – so if you stick with that door, you *still* have a 1 in 3 chance of winning.

It therefore stands to reason that if you switch to the other, since probabilities of all possible events must add up to 1, you have a 2 in 3 chance of winning. So you're twice as likely to win if you switch doors.

Essentially, the host is merging the two other doors into one, by opening the one he *knows* has no prize – which is another explanation for why switching to the other door will give you a 2 in 3 chance of winning.

PUZZLE 179

The policy has *no* effect – the likelihood of any child being born a boy or a girl remains constant, no matter what! All that happens is that some families aren't permitted to have so many children.

PUZZLE 180

Six – there is just the one sister!

PUZZLE 181

1 in 3, not 1 in 2 as might be expected. The possibilities for the genders of his children are boy-boy, boy-girl, girl-boy and girl-girl. But we can eliminate boy-boy, since we know he has a girl, so the chance he has *two* girls is 1 in 3.

PUZZLE 182

The couples already know one another, so the options are for each person to exchange anywhere from 0 to 8 cards. Andrea must therefore exchange the same number of cards as someone else, since there are only 9 options in total.

The person who exchanged 8 cards has to be in a couple with the person who exchanged 0 cards, otherwise that person could only have exchanged 7 cards at maximum. Similarly, the person who exchanged 7 cards is with the person who exchanged 1 card, and so on – so the couples exchanged 8 and 0 cards, 7 and 1 cards, 6 and 2 cards, and 5 and 3 cards. So Bob must have received 4 cards.

PUZZLE 183

I bet on 5, 10, 15, 20, 25, 30 and 35, which is 7 out of 37 options. So my odds are 7 in 37.

PUZZLE 184

$1/6 × 1/6 × 1/6 × 1/6 × 1/6 = 1/7776$

PUZZLE 185

There is a $(1/2)^8 = 1/256$ chance of all heads, and the same for tails, so 1/128 for *either* heads or tails

PUZZLE 186

The winning possibilities are win-win, win-lose and lose-win. So they are $(1/10 × 1/10) + (1/10 × 9/10) + (9/10 × 1/10) = 1/100 + 9/100 + 9/100 = 19/100$

PUZZLE 187

PUZZLE 188

PUZZLE 189

PUZZLE 190

E	F	G	B	D	C	A
D	A	E	G	C	F	B
C	B	D	A	E	G	F
A	G	B	C	F	D	E
F	D	A	E	G	B	C
B	C	F	D	A	E	G
G	E	C	F	B	A	D

PUZZLE 191

PUZZLE 192

3	2	1	28	29	30	51	52	81
4	23	24	27	32	31	50	53	80
5	22	25	26	33	48	49	54	79
6	21	36	35	34	47	46	55	78
7	20	37	38	43	44	45	56	77
8	19	18	39	42	59	58	57	76
9	16	17	40	41	60	61	62	75
10	15	14	67	66	65	64	63	74
11	12	13	68	69	70	71	72	73

PUZZLE 193

3 5   1

3	1	2	4	5
4	2	5	3	1
5	3	1	2	4
1	4	3	5	2	2
2	5	4	1	3

2   2   3

PUZZLE 194

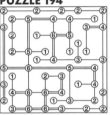

PUZZLE 195

  A   A   B

	C	A		B	
A		B	C		C
C			B	A	
B | B | A | | | C |
B | | B | C | A | | A

     C   C

PUZZLE 196

1	5	2	4	7	6	3
6	4	5	7	1	3	2
2	1	7	3	4	5	6
5	2	1	6	3	7	4
7	3	6	2	5	4	1
4	7	3	1	6	2	5
3	6	4	5	2	1	7

PUZZLE 197

1	3	6	2	5	4
2	1	4	6	3	5
6	5	3	1	4	2
4	6	2	5	1	3
3	2	5	4	6	1
5	4	1	3	2	6

PUZZLE 198

5	9		8	7		7	8	1	2
9	7		2	1		8	6	9	7	3
	8	9	7			9	8		7	9
	1	7	3		6	7	9	8		8	7
9	3		1	3	7	5		7	8	9
7	2			9	8			2	3	1
	6	1	7	4	9		6	4		6	9
	4	7	9	8			8	9		5	7

PUZZLE 199

PUZZLE 200

The secret is to make sure the two slowest people cross together – this involves *both* the initial two people who cross the bridge coming back at some point. So:

Have Xavier and Walder cross the bridge, taking 2 minutes.

Have Walder cross back, taking 1 minute.

Have Zeus and Yolanda cross over, taking 8 minutes.

Have Xavier cross back, taking 2 minutes.

Have Xavier and Walder cross the bridge, taking 2 minutes.

PUZZLE 201

```
        3
     2     3
   4 6 3 1 2 5 2 5
   5 1 2 4 3 6 6
 1 1 2 5 3 6 4 4 6
 6 6 3 1 5 4 2
 4 3 4 6 2 5 1
 2 2 5 4 6 1 3 1
     2     2
     3
```

PUZZLE 202

```
S C R A T C H   S T A T E
O   R   O   S   R   A
E L E C T R I C S H O C K
L   H   G   A       T
P A C I F I E R   M A I N
R   V       C   Y   C
  C I G A R E T T E
S   N   G       H   C
M I N G   E C O N O M I C
G       N   U   L   C
U N C O N D I T I O N A L
U   R   A   D   G   D
E P O C H   H O L Y D A Y
```

PUZZLE 203

PUZZLE 204

PUZZLE 205

PUZZLE 206

PUZZLE 207

It's a certainty

PUZZLE 208

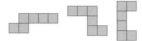

PUZZLE 209

Shape net 2 is different – the triangle points in the opposite direction to the other three cubes

PUZZLE 210

Pyramid b

PUZZLE 211

PUZZLE 212

47 cubes

Counting the top layer as level 1, this is made up of:
Level 1 cubes = 6
Level 2 cubes = 8
Level 3 cubes = 14
Level 4 cubes = 19

PUZZLE 213

36 cubes

Counting the top layer as level 1, this is made up of:
Level 1 cubes = 3
Level 2 cubes = 5
Level 3 cubes = 12
Level 4 cubes = 16